FOLKTALES OF *England*

 *Folktales*
OF THE WORLD

GENERAL EDITOR : RICHARD M. DORSON

FOLKTALES OF
England

EDITED BY
Katharine M. Briggs
AND
Ruth L. Tongue

THE UNIVERSITY OF CHICAGO PRESS

Library of Congress Catalog Card Number 65–18341
The University of Chicago Press, Chicago
Routledge & Kegan Paul, Ltd., London
The University of Toronto Press, Toronto 5, Canada
© 1965 by The University of Chicago. All rights reserved
Published 1965. Composed and printed in Great Britain
by William Clowes & Sons, Ltd., London and Beccles

Foreword

In Victorian England, folklore flowered as a living study in all save one major branch, the folktale. The ballad has proved England's strength and joy, ever since Bishop Percy brought forth his version of the *Reliques of Ancient English Poetry* in 1765; thereafter balladry developed its own cult. Those antiquaries who baptized the field of folklore in the first half of the nineteenth century concentrated their efforts on popular customs and usages. When the mammoth two-volume edition of John Brand's *Observations on Popular Antiquities*, edited by Sir Henry Ellis, Keeper of Manuscripts of the British Museum, was published in London in 1813, its vast, disorderly assemblage of "bygones" captivated English intellectuals. The interest kindled by these tomes eventually led to the devising of the word "folk-lore" in 1846 by antiquary William John Thoms and, after the fresh stimulus supplied by the anthropologist E. B. Tylor, to the formation of a vigorous Folk-Lore Society in 1878. From 1878 until the outbreak of the First World War, the society and its stellar figures, enormously gifted private scholars such as Andrew Lang and Sidney Hartland, Sir George Laurence Gomme and Edward Clodd and Alfred Nutt—who each served as president—developed folklore into an acknowledged science. The influence of folklore science extended into many fields of learning—the classics and anthropology, history and literature, philology and psychology, and even affected imperial policy, for colonial administrators around the globe collected folklore to understand better the peoples they governed.

In spite of changed theories, the central emphasis of English

v

folklore studies remained upon custom. The rationalist antiquaries of the eighteenth and early nineteenth centuries uncovered
curious specimens of ancient rites and feasts as examples of
pagan and papist superstition. The late nineteenth-century school
of anthropological folklorists dissected archaic customs as survivals of primitive stages in human culture and thought. Today
the English Folklore Society continues to issue its series of British
Calendar Customs, stemming directly from the *Popular Antiquities* of John Brand.[1]

Amidst the ferment and excitement aroused by the new science
of folklore, the folktale necessarily came in for its share of
attention. The impact of the famous collection begun by the
brothers Grimm in 1812 made itself felt in England, as in all
Europe, and a still standard edition of their *Household Tales*
appeared in 1884 in the English translation of Margaret Hunt,
with a lengthy introduction by Andrew Lang, who analyzed the
primitive ideas concealed in the tales. Yet the fact had become
painfully evident, by the close of Victoria's reign, that the treasure
trove of fairy tales unearthed for nearly every European country,
in replica of the Grimms' discovery in Germany, would not be
found in England. In Scotland and Ireland vast stockpiles of
Märchen had been, and would continue to be, collected from the
mouths of villagers. Why had a blight struck merry England?

No one has yet produced a satisfactory answer. From settlers of
English stock in the southern Appalachians, American collectors
suddenly chanced, in the 1920's, upon a wealth of magical folk
narrative, centering on Jack the Giant Killer. But English collectors have gathered no such harvest. In 1890, when Edwin
Sidney Hartland assembled a volume comparable to the present
one, *English Fairy and Other Folk Tales*, he located only half
a dozen "nursery tales" to place among his seventy-two stories
and culled the rest from "sagas" about local events, fairies,
ghosts, witches, giants, and devils, including a packet of eight

---

[1] Sketches of the English folklore movement are given in my articles
in the *Journal of American Folklore*, "The First Group of British Folklorists," LXVIII (1955), 1–8, 333–40; " The Eclipse of Solar Mythology,"
LXVIII (1955), 394–416; and "The Great Team of English Folklorists,"
LXIV (1951), 1–10.

"drolls," the term then current for comical tales. (The proportions have remained fairly constant in the present work, proof enough how few *Märchen* have come to light in England after a century and a half of scattered searching.) Hartland, a scholar of the first rank, remained always faithful to his sources and printed his narratives exactly as they appeared in the chapbooks, county collections, table-books, and journal of the Folk-Lore Society. Few of these sources presented the tales in the precise words of their tellers, for the concept of scientific accuracy in field-work would be a long time in gaining acceptance. Yet an oral past lay behind them, as Hartland unerringly perceived in making selections from Thomas Keightley's *The Fairy Mythology* (1828), Mrs. Bray's *A Description of the Part of Devonshire Bordering on the Tamar and the Tavy* (three volumes, 1836), and Robert Hunt's Cornish collection, *Popular Romances from the West of England* (two volumes, 1865). Other favourite resources included such stalwart compendiums as the *Shropshire Folk-Lore* of Charlotte S. Burne (1883) and William Henderson's *Notes on the Folk-Lore of the Northern Counties of England and the Borders* (1866). Some of the county collections, however, were published subsequent to Hartland's gleaning.

A volume similar in aim issued by Joseph Jacobs that same year achieved more popular success but fell below Hartland's standards. Jacobs, a knowledgeable folklorist who stressed diffusion rather than survival in folktales and is known for a valuable edition of Aesop's *Fables*, published *English Fairy Tales* in 1890 and *More English Fairy Tales* in 1894. To compensate for the lack of available oral texts in England, Jacobs slipped across the border to lowland Scotland for selections, roamed to the United States and Australia, and even adapted ballad stories into tales. He rewrote all his sources to please children. Wanting to have and eat his cake, he provided an appendix with data on his altering and blending of incidents, and cited some parallels in Great Britain and on the Continent. This veneer of scholarship gave Jacobs's volumes an undeserved claim to authenticity. Unlike most other purveyors of children's tales, Jacobs knew better, and defended himself, particularly in the preface to the second volume, with assertions that the Grimms and Asbjörnsen

had used printed sources and revamped stories, and that any
writer familiar with his native tradition could indulge in the
same storytelling license enjoyed by the folk. In the history of
folklore studies, no claim has proved more spurious and harmful
than this assertion of license to tamper with texts. Jacobs's vain
comparison of his *English Fairy Tales* with the *Märchen* of the
Grimm brothers—a fashionable comparison in many countries
over the past century—had no substance. The Grimms in Germany, and Asbjörnsen and Moe in Norway, pioneered in the
direct collection of oral folktales from storytellers, but Jacobs
engaged in no such field-work.

The inferiority complex in folktale matters under which England has so long suffered proceeds from the aristocratic status of
Märchen. Hartland and Jacobs felt the need to include "fairy
tales" in their titles, the term adopted in English as an equivalent
for *Märchen*. These lengthy, adventuresome, highly structured
fictions filled with magical episodes and royal personages seemed
indeed prize treasures when the Grimms first heralded them to
the world. By contrast, the brief, formless *Sagen*, or legends, tied
to local places, events, and characters, appeared of little general
interest, and the Grimms' *Deutsche Sagen* (1816–18) was never
translated into English. Only in 1959 did recognition come to the
lowly legend, when the newly organized International Society for
Folk Narrative Research appointed a committee to investigate
and co-ordinate legend studies and catalogues. Yet for legendary
traditions, and legend scholarship, England can point with pride
to the beginnings of folklore inquiries.

As early as 1828, in his work on *The Fairy Mythology*, Thomas
Keightley explored one branch of local tradition. "Fairy" in his
title applied not to *Märchen* but to reports about elflike beings
who were regarded as real. Keightley was born in Ireland but
came to London to make a Grub Street livelihood producing
schoolbooks, histories, and editions of popular authors. Wracked
with illness, boastful yet naïve, Keightley published in *The
Fairy Mythology* and *Tales and Popular Fictions* (1834) two
original treatises on folk narrative deserving recognition. He contributed four fairy legends known from his youth to the pioneer
collection, *Fairy Legends and Traditions of the South of Ireland*

issued by his fellow Anglo-Irishman, T. Crofton Croker, in
1825; later, after breaking with Croker, he confessed to decorat-
ing them, and to transplanting a German legend onto Irish soil.
But Keightley quickly perceived the rules of folklore research
and the nature of folklore materials. For *The Fairy Mythology*
he assembled scattered sources from all over Europe and the
Middle East—he claimed to know over twenty languages—and
made their connections apparent. To compile his substantial
section on England, he scoured twelfth- and thirteenth-century
chronicles by William of Newbridge and Gervase of Tilbury;
picked up the trail again in the Elizabethan age with a chapbook
on Robin Goodfellow used by Shakespeare and the discussion
of bogies in the 1665 edition of Reginald Scot's *The Discoverie of
Witchcraft*; extracted a few nuggets from John Aubrey's seventeenth-century notebooks; and so made his way to his own day.
In the later, expanded edition of 1850 Keightley fattened his
offering from interim reports of local collectors. Thus he wrote:

> There is no stronger proof of the neglect of what Mr. Thoms
> has very happily designated "Folk-lore" in this country, than
> the fact of there having been no account given anywhere of the
> Pixies or Pisgies of Devonshire and Cornwall, till within these
> last few years. In the year 1836, Mrs. Bray, a lady well known
> as the author of several novels, and wife of a clergyman at Tavis-
> tock, published, in a series of letters to Robert Southey, interest-
> ing descriptions of the part of Devonshire bordering on the
> Tamar and the Tavy. In this work there is given an account of
> the Pixies, from which we derive the following information:[2]

With such assistance Keightley was able to chart the course
of the "vairies, farisees, frairies, farys," as they were alternatively
called, through southern and northern counties, including several
narrations he himself had heard. After the collectors he moved
to the poets, from Chaucer to Spenser, who had known fairy
traditions at first hand. All these items of fairylore Keightley
sought to fit into a scheme of racial geography. Strongly in-
fluenced by the *Deutsche Mythologie* of Jacob Grimm (which

---

[2] Thomas Keightley, *The Fairy Mythology, illustrative of the Romance
and Superstition of various Countries* (London, 1850), p. 298.

would be translated into English in three volumes by James S. Stallybrass, 1882–83), he theorized that the fairy belief descended from a primitive "Gotho-Germanic" religion, and thence spread to the weaker "Celtic-Cymric" peoples. Accordingly the Norwegian *nisse* and German *kobold* preceded the Irish fairy and Scottish brownie. The family relationship was, however, apparent, and the fairies of England, like their northern brethren, were "divided into two classes—the rural Elves, inhabiting the woods, fields, mountains, and caverns; and the domestic or house-spirits, usually called Hobgoblins and Robin Goodfellows."[3]

The explorations of Keightley prepared the way for a major synthesis by Hartland, written in the changed atmosphere of post-Darwinian researches. His *The Science of Fairy Tales, An Inquiry into Fairy Mythology*, published in 1891, is an ingenious and masterful exposition of the laws and formulas perceptible in traditions about the elfin beings of legend and the heroes and heroines of popular tales. Hartland supplemented Keightley's materials with collections issued in the preceding forty years— his bibliography of sources covered twelve pages—and applied the investigative technique of the anthropological folklorists. He proposed to show how the fairy belief reflected savage ideas about magic and demonology which still survived in the state of civilization. Fairies, ghosts, witches, the gods of classical myths, the ogres of popular sagas all ultimately derived from the imaginative conjurations of primitive man, who guarded himself against these dread beings with taboo, charm, sacrifice, and propitiatory rite. Hartland quoted the *London Daily Telegraph* of May 17, 1884, as reporting the arrest of two women in Clonmel who stole into a neighbor's house and placed on a hot shovel a three-year-old child they suspected of being a changeling left by the fairies. Examples such as these proved to Hartland and his fellow folklorists in the wake of Tylor that the notions of the universe once held by savages still persisted among the "lower orders." In *Märchen* too, which were fictions absorbing ancient beliefs, and often took the form of sagas (legends), the same order of unnatural or supernatural creatures could plainly

[3] Keightley, *Ibid.*, p. 281.

be seen. Hartland discussed at length the worldwide *Märchen* centering on a swan-maiden who is changed from a bird to a beautiful woman when she removes her feathers to go swimming; he concludes that a totemic worship of a goddess underlies the story. The *Märchen* hero in Fairyland who is unaware of time passing corresponds to the Sleeping Hero of national legend who succours his people in time of crisis; both figures descend from a heathen god never totally suppressed by Christianity. Jack the Giant Killer and King Arthur are one.

In a splendid opening chapter Hartland described "The Art of Story-Telling," giving extracts and illustrations of narrative practices from many cultures, and stressing their uniformity and faithful adherence to tradition.

> Whether told by men to men in the bazaar or the coffee-house of the East, or by old men or women to children in the sacred recesses of the European home, or by men to a mixed assembly during the endless nights of the Arctic Circle, or in the huts of the tropical forest...the endeavour to render to the audience just that which the speaker has himself received from his predecessors is paramount.[4]

And Hartland cautioned the collector in turn to ensure that the "documents are gathered direct from the lips of the illiterate story-teller" and set down with all their imperfections and coarseness. Only thus could contributions to the science of folklore be registered. Literary renderings of traditions might serve to amuse, but had little other purpose.

This ringing declaration, made in 1891, can still serve as a creed for the folklorist today. The method of precise field work demanded by Hartland is unquestioned in scholarly circles. Hartland's theoretical premises are more debatable. He contended that the science of fairy tales dealt not with a juvenile world of fantasy and entertainment, but with a primitive universe still visible in the nineteenth century, in *Märchen* and sagas alike. The *Märchen* so prized by continental scholars turn out to be but an offshoot of the heroic legends so deep-rooted in England.

[4] Edwin Sidney Hartland, *The Science of Fairy Tales. An Inquiry into Fairy Mythology* (London, 1891), pp. 20–21.

The legend studies of Keightley and Hartland depended of
course on legend collectors. Who can be called the first deliberate
collector of English traditional tales? A clear-cut answer may
not be possible, since the question really hinges on the degree
of accuracy one demands, and throughout the nineteenth century
the concept of fidelity to the oral text never won a complete
victory. However, a first of a kind must go to Mrs. Bray and
her three volumes, issued in 1836 and reissued in 1879 in two
volumes under its best-known title, *The Borders of the Tamar
and the Tavy*, with a more revealing subtitle: "Their Natural
History, Manners, Customs, Superstitions, Scenery, Antiquities,
Eminent Persons, etc. In a Series of Letters to the Late Robert
Southey, Esq." The widow of a clergyman and antiquarian of
Dartmoor, Edward Atkyns Bray, and a writer of reputation in
her own right, Mrs. Bray undertook her epistolary narrative of
Devonshire traditions in response to a fertile suggestion made by
her friend the poet Southey, in a letter he wrote her in 1831.

> I should like to see from you what English literature yet
> wants—a good specimen of local history, not the antiquities only,
> nor the natural history, nor both together (as in White's delight-
> ful book about Selbourne), nor the statistics, but everything
> about a parish that can be made interesting—all of its history,
> traditions, and manners that can be saved from oblivion...not
> omitting some of those 'short and simple annals' of domestic
> life which ought not to be forgotten.[5]

Southey here was proposing a new ingredient in a well-estab-
lished and prospering English genre, the county survey of Roman
and Saxon ruins (antiquities) coupled with commentary on
geologic and topographic features (natural history). Now he
added the local customs and beliefs which in 1846 Thoms would
designate folklore. They were themselves a species of antiquities
—the term "folklore" replaced Brand's phrase "popular antiquities"—and their local associations wedded them to scenic
landmarks.

The total quantity of folk tradition included by Mrs. Bray in

[5] Mrs A. E. Bray, *The Borders of the Tamar and the Tavy* (London,
1879), I, p. vii.

her flowery musings was not large, but her method of discussing local traditions directly rather than embroidering them in fictional sketches was new, and this impressed later collectors. One letter she devoted entirely to the pixies or "pisgies" of Devon, in another she set forth some fabulous legends about Sir Francis Drake, and in a third she spoke about "vestiges of ancient superstitions." From her mixed brew to a volume wholly concerned with local traditions was an easy step.

A case could be made for James Orchard Halliwell (later Halliwell-Phillipps) as a first, since his *Popular Rhymes and Nursery Tales* of 1849 included a sheaf of seventeen "Fireside Nursery Stories." Halliwell was feverishly active in the antiquarian societies of the mid-nineteenth century, and some of his voluminous productions spilled over into folklore. While he gleaned such tales as "Jack and the Giants" and "Tom Hickathrift" from chapbooks, others he obtained from oral recitals in Yorkshire and Oxfordshire. Halliwell did not name his storytellers or follow their words literally, but he realized "how very desirable it would be to procure the traditional tale as related by the English peasantry."

The most complete collection of traditional tales gathered in England was made by Robert Hunt in Cornwall. Hunt began noting local stories some thirty years before he published two volumes of them in 1865 under the title, *Popular Romances of the West of England; or, The Drolls, Traditions and Superstitions of Old Cornwall*. As a child Hunt penned wild Cornish legends in his notebooks; in 1829 he spent ten months in a walking tour across Cornwall, deliberately ferreting out "romances" and "drolls"; in the following years he listened sympathetically to the tales of miners and peasants in his capacity as secretary of the Royal Cornwall Polytechnic Society; and in 1862 he even engaged an itinerant postmaster and poet to scour the countryside for remaining traditions. Other, lesser collectors turned over their hoards to Hunt. This long-range, intensive, and systematic folktale quest still stands alone in the history of English folklore. Hunt states that even in the span between 1829 and 1835 traditions had vanished, and by 1862 his postmaster-collector found only slim pickings. He himself set out just in time to encounter two of the old "droll-tellers," as the wandering minstrels of Cornwall were called.

Cornwall offered a particularly attractive hunting ground for an English folklorist in view of its isolated position as the southernmost county, separated from the rest of England by the river Tamar, and, in Hunt's youth, still traversed only by primitive conveyances. In addition, the Celtic character of the Cornish, with their recently vanished language, added mystery to the quest; Hunt believed that the Cornish giant was a "true Celt," showing affinities with Scottish giants, and in the older traditions he imagined he was recapturing the ancient Celtic mythology. Modern tales were colored by the Cornish occupations of fishing and tin mining.

Hunt made some advances from the literary and romantic treatment of Mrs. Bray, whose work he knew. He kept the portrayal of the landscape under partial restraint and he arranged his contents as a series of individual traditions, divided under main headings—Giants, Fairies, Tregeagle, Lost Cities, The Saints, Holy Wells, Demons and Spectres, King Arthur, Mermaids, Fishermen and Sailors—with his first volume devoted to mythic and his second to historic traditions. The legends, however, are elaborated and paraphrased; the concept of the oral text is not yet recognized, nor are storytellers identified.

This wide cache of 337 stories and items of superstition contains nothing but believed traditions and traditional beliefs. The fairies loom large, with twenty-nine entries devoted to them. Ghosts, demons, witches, and bogies abound, and historical personages are cast in the role of sorcerers and wizards, whether the wicked landlord Tregeagle, or the diabolic hero Sir Francis Drake. Landmarks localize the traditional incidents, which cling to rocks, wells, lakes, churches, and castles. These stories have nothing in common with the *Märchen* of the brothers Grimm, although Hunt calls them, rightly, the "genuine household tales of the people."[6]

Only one collector other than Hunt broke with the conventional pattern of the county fieldbook to concentrate on tales.

[6] Robert Hunt, *Popular Romances of the West of England*, First Series (London, 1865), p. xxiii.

This was Sidney Oldall Addy, an Oxford graduate resident in
Sheffield, who had published a glossary of Sheffield words for
the English Dialect Society, interspersed with folklore items
(1888, 1891), and a history of local antiquities, *The Hall of
Waltheof, or The Early Condition and Settlement of Hallam-
shire* (1893). These interests led him deeper into the collecting
of local traditions, and after some six years of foraging Addy
brought together his texts in 1895 under a title obviously indebted
both to the Grimms and Tylor, *Household Tales with Other
Traditional Remains. Collected in the Counties of York, Lincoln, Derby and Nottingham.* Most of the fifty-two narratives
fell into the category of the brief, localized legend rather than
the European popular fiction, and dealt largely with the fairies,
witches and wizards, and the Devil or the Old Lad.

   This circumstance merely reinforced the folklore theories Addy
derived from his countrymen. He had independently reached
Hartland's conclusion that fairies, witches, and ghosts over-
lapped and coalesced, and pointed back to savage superstitions.
In the believed tales, and the scattered beliefs about the natural
world and calendar year he placed under "Traditional Remains,"
Addy thought he perceived much evidence to support the doc-
trine of survivals. Approvingly, he quoted from the *Quarterly
Review* a definition of the "modern word folk-lore" as "the
geology of the human race."[7] He cites Hartland's *The Science
of Fairy Tales* and the Stallybrass edition of Grimm's *Deutsche
Mythologie*, and is in correspondence with "Dr. Tylor of
Oxford." All their ideas confirm his findings. Folklore does indeed preserve the relics of pagan ritual and worship. The Morris
dance suggested an original dusky race. Three tall, thin women
with hourglasses in their hands, seen by a Derbyshire villager,
standing in a line on the common at Cold-Aston, must be the
Norns or Fates, foretelling a death within three hours. Miners
in north Derbyshire who leave a hundredweight of coal each
week for the fairies are but one instance of modern worshipers
offering firstfruits to local divinities. Jack Otter in a Lincolnshire
legend is Odin, the hated one, and so is Robin Hood—and by

---

[7] Sidney Oldall Addy, *Household Tales with Other Traditional Remains*
(London, Sheffield, 1895), p. xxii

the etymological equations dear to the Victorians, Addy cor-
related Robin Hood's merry men with the Norse pantheon.
Again, Old Tup in the comic ballad of "The Derby Ram" is
none other than the giant Ymir in the Edda.

So reasoned Addy. On some points we can agree. The merging
of the fairy, witch, and ghost concepts in the sixteenth and seventeenth centuries has been elaborated in rich detail in our time
by Katharine Briggs. And the intertwining of community
legend, supernatural experience, and popular superstition is today
well recognized. But the analogy of peasant with savage beliefs,
so prized by the Victorians, no longer wins acceptance.

From the viewpoint of method, Addy made definite advances,
although he still falls short of modern requirements. He took all
his texts from oral tradition, but some were written down for
him by the tellers, and he made a few verbal changes, such as
introducing the hallowed phrase "Once upon a time"—a more
serious addition than one might suspect, since such a formula
introduces a *Märchen* but not a legend. Addy gave the village
provenience of the tales, but did not name informants or seek
hard for parallels.

While Hunt and Addy collected chiefly legends and beliefs,
the typical Victorian clergyman, or his wife, who was busily
assembling the county fieldbooks sought all scraps of lore surviving within the district. A number of these fieldbooks were
printed in the second half of the nineteenth century, becoming
vademecums for the library theorists; all contained some
legendary tales, usually in paraphrase. The three earliest came
from the north: William Henderson's *Notes on the Folk Lore of
the Northern Counties of England and the Borders* (1866); John
Harland and T. T. Wilkinson's *Lancashire Folk-Lore, illustrative of the Superstitious Beliefs and Practices, Local Customs
and Usages of the People of the County Palatine* (1867); and
Charles Hardwick's *Traditions, Superstitions and Folk-Lore
(chiefly Lancashire and the North of England)* (1872). Others
followed, larger and bulkier, with chief acclamation going to the
Shropshire Folk-Lore of Charlotte S. Burne in 1883. All held to
the same pattern, offering chapters on such matters as omens
and auguries, dreams and divinations, fairies and bogles, ghosts

and devils, witchcraft and magic, superstitions of plants and animals, common usages and holy day ceremonies, well-worship and divining rods. They bore the air of fondled scrapbooks, pasted together with loving care from earlier manuscripts, newspaper clippings, field jottings, and literary cutouts. All these volumes continued and confirmed the English emphasis on local custom and local tradition.[8]

The constant desire, nevertheless, to emulate the Grimms' *Märchen* is seen in an appendix to Henderson's collection titled "Household Tales" and prepared by the prolific Sabine Baring-Gould, an Anglican clergyman. After making his deference to the Grimms, he plots out "story radicals," or skeletal synopses of various international folktales. For example, the story of Jack the Giant Killer is placed under this heading:

Sect. III.—Men in Conflict with Supernatural Beings
A. Men obtain the Mastery by Cunning
  I. Jack the Giant Killer root
    1. A man is matched with giants or devils.
    2. He deceives them by his superior cunning.
    3. He makes them kill themselves.

Baring-Gould thus ingeniously anticipated the *Type-Index of the Folk-Tale*, which Antti Aarne and Stith Thompson would issue in 1928 as a system for identifying the widely diffused folktales of Europe. However, the slender stock of English popular fictions could scarcely provide the launching platform for such a catalogue, eventually constructed from Germanic and Finnish texts and their analogues. Nor were all the sixteen tales, largely from Yorkshire and Devonshire, true *Märchen*; four were legendary, one was a parrot anecdote, another a riddle-tale (see No. 43, "Mr. Fox's Courtship" in this volume), and yet another a lying tale. Baring-Gould would have been on firmer ground if he had attempted to classify local legends.

When a cycle of tales did come to light in the county collections, it took the form of anecdotes attached to a local personage.

---

[8] The Folk-Lore Society sponsored a series on county folklore from printed sources, but these, while of unquestioned value, did not involve fieldwork (Vols. I-VII, 1893–1914).

2

In Ella Leather's *The Folk-Lore of Herefordshire* (1912), to which Hartland contributed an introduction, a cluster of brief stories dealt with Jack o' Kent, who may or may not have existed as a fugitive on the Welsh border. He emerges as a wizard outwitting the Devil in various partnerships and bargains. But in characteristic English fashion, these familiar international tales are sharply localized in Kentchurch, where people were wont to say, "As great as the Devil and Jack o' Kent."

Besides the county compendiums, such periodicals as *Notes and Queries* and *Folk-Lore* occasionally carried English oral tales. The second volume of *Folk-Lore* (1891) offered a glimpse of hidden treasures, in "Legends of the Cars," a swatch of ten oral narratives from north Lincolnshire, collected by Marie Clothilde Balfour, an aunt by marriage of Robert Louis Stevenson. Before they were drained, the Cars of Lindsey in the Ancholme Valley had been wide swamps bordering small streams, desolate and dreary, and cut off from the modern world. Their inhabitants, grave, long-featured, suspicious and superstitious, speaking in almost pure Saxon, related wild and rambling histories of heathen rites and the powers of "woe-women," in which they seemed still to half-believe. In the tale of "The Stranger's Share," a dweller in the Cars recalls how an older generation had neglected the "tiddy people" by going to church, and forgetting to lay out the first fruits of the harvest for them on flat stones, or to drop a crumb for them on the fireplace. So the Strangers took away their favors from the people of the Cars. "Tha men'd took to th' gin, an' the wimmen to th' op'um; tha favers shuk 'em allers, an' th' brats wor yaller 'n illgrowed." This indeed was their condition. These powerful legends (see "The Green Mist," No. 12 in this volume) pointed to unsuspected currents of narrative lore.

In recent years the cause of English folklore, depressed between the two world wars, has regained momentum. The investigation of fairy lore was continued in two notable studies by Katharine M. Briggs, *The Anatomy of Puck* (1959) and *Pale Hecate's Team* (1962). Although the first dealt primarily with the fairy belief and the second with witch beliefs, the two works are complementary, both derived from the author's doctoral dissertation at

Oxford. Dr. Briggs scoured the sixteenth and seventeenth centuries for evidence of folklore, examining popular sources like chapbooks, ballads, court trials, and magic tracts; learned authors like Reginald Scot and Robert Burton; and Elizabethan and Jacobean poets and dramatists from Shakespeare to Drayton. As Keightley developed *The Fairy Mythology* from the concept of popular antiquities, and Hartland based *The Science of Fairy Tales* upon the theory of uniform cultural evolution, so Briggs has conceived *The Anatomy of Puck* from the premises of intellectual history. Beliefs are related to the dominant ideas and cosmology of the period; literature is viewed in its social setting; the historical forces of church, state, court, university, and manor are taken into account. Briggs cleverly pursues the interaction of learning and lore; the mixing of pagan, Christian, and folk elements; the merging of supernatural creatures as fairy glides into ghost, ghost into demon, demon into ogre. Literature dips impartially into classical mythology and country traditions. Astrology and alchemy hover between science and sorcery. The magician and the witch, the fairy and the goddess shuttle between the natural and supernatural worlds. Each generation, she writes, accounted for the decline of the fairies by the victory of its dominant form of belief.

The sixteenth and seventeenth centuries intrigue the folklorist, for the covert lore of the countryside was then bursting into public view, with the relaxing of the Church's restraints and the emergence of the yeoman writer. The evil witchcraft controversy, to which King James I contributed his *Daemonologie* (1597), incited polemical tracts and court proceedings strewn with folklore notions. In Elizabethan times every Englishman was basically a countryman and comprehended, if he had not actually imbibed, the supernatural lore of the village.

Detecting the traditions of folklore in literary, learned, and popular sources requires a firm grasp of folklore science. For documentation Dr. Briggs provides the appropriate motifs in Stith Thompson's *Motif-Index of Folk Literature*, and she constantly cites texts comparable to her printed extracts of oral traditions collected in the nineteenth and twentieth centuries; these she records in appendixes in both volumes. Thus from a work

of 1674, *Bovet's Pandaemonium, or The Devil's Cloyster*, Briggs
reprints an account of a fairy market seen by a traveler at Blackdown, near Taunton, in Somerset. Save that they were smaller
than ordinary country folk, the fairies could have passed for
farmers vending their wares. As the traveler approached, they
became invisible, although he felt their buffets; on the other
side of the market, he again saw them from afar; ever after he
found himself lame. Three centuries later Ruth Tongue heard of
a similar experience befalling a farmer at the same hill, save that
this one fared well (see No. 10, "Pixy Fair" in this volume).
Tales such as these all belong to legendry, or what the Swedish
folklorist Carl von Sydow has called the *memorat*, the personal
account of an experience with the supernatural.

Briggs distinguishes four main species of fairy beings, thus
doubling Keightley's categories: the trooping fairies, who always
appeared, even in their frolics, as a disciplined and motivated
group; the rough hobgoblin; mermaids and nature fairies; and
giants. Of these, the last two kinds were rarely reported in
England. This broad classification covers more than merely
diminutive beings, and the assumption is that all these anthropo-
morphic creatures originally descended from pagan deities.

In these rich puddings of folklore scholarship, the affinity between legend and belief and the continuity of supernatural lore
from the ancient past to the present day are brilliantly outlined.

Organized collecting does not exist in twentieth-century England as in Ireland, Scotland, and Wales. Even the string of
county fieldbooks assembled by devoted amateurs has ended. But
some striking examples of English oral narrative have nevertheless come to light. In 1938 Edward M. Wilson, of Emmanuel
College, Cambridge University, who had been active in the
Eastern Counties Folklore Society, published in *Folk-Lore* more
than a score of tales he had taken down from local people in
Westmorland. These he presented as exact texts. Many proved to
be international types, but not *Märchen*; rather they were short
humorous anecdotes and trickster stories. A cycle of special
interest revolved around "Tales of Masters and Men," that is,
the small farmer and his unmarried hired laborer, whose relationship provided a natural theme for artful dodges and come-

uppances. One cante-fable, "The Hungry Mowers" (No. 83 in this volume) includes a long drawn-out verse sung by ill-fed laborers; when their diet is improved, they change to a lively rhythm as their work speeds up. The same tale was known among Southern slaves in the United States, where the plantation owner and his favored house slave also exemplify the master and man relationship.

Then in 1963 and 1964 the long drought ended with two astonishing volumes of local folk history, *Tales from the Fens* and *More Tales from the Fens.* These fifty-seven traditional memories were written down by a gifted Fen storyteller, W. H. Barrett, and edited with historical notes by Enid Porter, curator of the Cambridge and County Folk Museum; but there is no question of their oral nature, and Dr. Briggs has tape-recorded three of Barrett's stories for the present book (Nos. 23, 55, 91).

No traditions could be more highly localized than these public-house yarns set in the grim swamp country of Cambridgeshire and Norfolk, where a hard-luck but hardy people contended against a hostile environment and oppressive landowners. Cherished and familiar in the Fens, these chapters of oral history would have no reason to wander across the Fen borders, even when they were recounted to sympathetic Cambridge dons, or gregarious strangers like Mark Twain. True, Mark's own American tall tale is still remembered in the Fens (see No. 91 in this volume), but only in the context of his visit. Supernatural motifs of haunted spots and gypsies' curses, witches' maledictions and prenatal birthmarks recur, for they were part of the Fenman's life, but it is the life itself, in its terrible and comical moments, that gives body to the narrations. In the reminiscence called "Hunger in the Fens," a wry account of a regal dinner prepared for a starving Fen family from the head of an emaciated cow and lumpish leftover flour, the social historian can find meticulous details of famine conditions in the 1840's. Yet the note of social protest is muffled; when outsiders attempt to organize, Fenmen and landlords join to run them out of town.

Sometimes a story can be traced directly back to the eighteenth century, as a ninety-year-old narrator recalls hearing it from his father or grandfather. Historical happenings of a distant past are kept vivid by the Fenmen, who discourse of medieval monks, hired German soldiers, imported Dutch engineers, French prisoners, Irish workers, the escape of King Charles I. Recent excavations of a Roman site have apparently validated a Fen chronicle. Brutality and violence are commonplace, with impalings, crucifixions, gibbetings, and butcherings tossed off as natural occurrences in an older, harsher day. Trivial incidents and obscure characters alternate with great events and illustrious names. The historical tradition is one of the most neglected forms of folklore. In the Fen and the Car tales, England is seen to be as wealthy in this form as Iceland with her sagas.

Today folklorists are beginning to recognize the vitality of oral narratives other than the vaunted *Märchen*. Besides the local legend, *memorat*, and historical tale, several varieties of oral humor flourish in modern life. The joke, the shaggy dog, the tall tale, the numskull story abound among educated city folk and deserve acceptance in the corpus of folktales. Little attempt has yet been made to gather and examine these forms, although Eric Partridge did devote a book to *The 'Shaggy Dog' Story, Its Origin, Nature and Development* (1953). This humorous, modern story lore belongs not to regions but to a mobile society, and easily crisscrosses the Atlantic between England and America. Macabre legends also thrive in the modern metropolis. The newly uncovered modern legend of "The Stolen Corpse" (see No. 48 in this volume) was first reported in England in 1963, and within the year it had been recorded in the United States. The present volume testifies to the vigor of the English folktale, and to the strength of local tradition and popular jest in England's country towns and industrial cities.[9]   RICHARD M. DORSON

In editing the notes of these folktales for the press, I have been greatly assisted by Hilda Webb, who performed the editorial work on Ernest W. Baughman's *A Type and Motif-Index of the Folktales of England and North America*. The index has been prepared by Betsy Greenlee Stampe.   R. M. D.

[9] Katharine Briggs has in preparation an exhaustive dictionary of English folk-narratives, described in her progress report, "Making a Dictionary of Folk-Tales," *Folklore*, LXXII (1961), 300-305. Ruth L. Tongue is bringing out a volume of her collections titled *Somerset Folklore*.

Introduction

The fairy stories of the old-fashioned *Märchen* type have almost disappeared from oral tradition in England. A few, however, are still told, and those collected in the late nineteenth century and early twentieth century are some of the finest in Europe. I have included in this collection a few of those which show all the signs of having been accurately transcribed in their local dialects. Perhaps "Tom Tit Tot" is the flower of them, but "The Green Mist," told to Mrs. Balfour by an old Lincolnshire Fenman and much less known than "Tom Tit Tot," is a good example of the weird Fenland imagination. "The Small-Tooth Dog" is a pleasantly homely version of "Beauty and the Beast," a tale rather rare in England; "The Black Bull of Norroway" type is commoner.

From literary references we know that a great many of the International Tale Types were once known in England. Two quoted by Shakespeare we have been able to recover in their entirety. In Malone's *Variorum Shakespeare* we find the story of Mr. Fox, with the catch phrase, "It is not so, nor it was not so, and God forbid it should be so," quoted by Benedick (*Much Ado About Nothing*, I, i). The cumulative inscription carved over the doors and staircase in the same tale, "Be bold, be bold, but not too bold," was used by Spenser (*The Faerie Queene*, III, ii). Miss Tongue found a late version of "Mr. Fox" in Somerset, and it is scattered in various forms over the country.

"Childe Rowland" was given by Jamieson in his *Illustrations of Northern Antiquities*, published in 1814. He had heard it from an Aberdeen tailor in his youth about 1770, and Motherwell in his *Minstrelsy Ancient and Modern* in 1827 said that it was still a nursery tale in Scotland. Scottish though it may be in its more modern form, it is clear that Shakespeare knew it in the heart of England. In the story Childe Rowland rescues his sister from the Dark Tower of Elfland, and when the Elf King comes in he cries out:

> Fee, fi, fo, fum,
> I smell the blood of a Christian man!
> Be he dead, be he living, with my brand
> I'll clash his harns from his harn-pan.

In *King Lear* (III, iv), Edgar says:

> Childe Rowland to the dark tower came,
> His word was still, Fie, foh and fum,
> I smell the blood of a British man.

We have no verbatim report of this tale; it was embellished according to the fashion of the time; and therefore I have not included it in this book, but it is of such great interest that it is worth giving a shortened version of it here. The best full telling of it is to be found in Jacobs' *English Fairy Tales*, where Jacobs has pruned some embroidery admittedly added by Jamieson. Childe is the old title given to a noble heir, and Jacobs suggests that we may find here some trace of the custom of Borough English, a custom we shall find touched on in *The Apple-Tree Man*.

Childe Rowland

There were once three king's sons, the youngest of whom was called Childe Rowland, and they had a sister called Burd Helen. One day, as the boys were playing football, Childe Rowland kicked the ball over the church. Burd Helen ran to fetch it, but never returned. At length the eldest brother set out to find her, and went, by his mother's advice, to learn from the Wizard Merlin what he should do. Merlin told him that when he got to Elfland he must chop off the head of anyone who spoke to him until he met Burd Helen, and that he must bite no bit nor drink no drop while he was in Elfland. He set out, but never returned. The second received the same advice, but fared no better. At length Childe Rowland, girded with his father's

*good sword, set out by the same way. Following Merlin's advice
he cut off the head of the King of Elfland's horseherd and cow-
herd, oxherd, swineherd, and henwife. Then he came to the
green fairy knowe and walked round it three times widdershins,
crying: "Open door! Open door!" The third time the door
opened, and he found himself in the Dark Tower of Elfland,
where there was neither sun nor moon and the walls shone with
gems. There in the great hall he found Burd Helen, who greeted
him sadly and told him that their brothers were dead. They
talked long, and Childe Rowland grew hungry and asked for
meat and drink. Burd Helen had no power to warn him, and she
brought him what he asked for; but before he drank he looked
to her, and remembered just in time. He dashed the cup to the
ground, and with an ogreish cry the Elf King came into the
hall. Childe Rowland drew his father's good sword, and they
fought together till he forced the Elf King to the ground, and
made him promise to restore his brothers to life, and set Burd
Helen free. The Elf King fetched a phial of red liquor, and
anointed the ears and eyelids, nostrils, lips, and fingertips of the
two Princes, so that they revived. Then he freed Burd Helen
from her spell, and they went home together in great joy.*

It will be seen that this is a variant of Tale Type 471, apparently
a popular tale in Shakespeare's time, for Peele uses a version of
it in *The Old Wives Tale*. Milton's *Comus* is founded on something of the same plot, the rescue of a sister by her brothers.

The Old Wives Tale is a treasury of references to tales which
have now been lost. "The Grateful Dead" (Type 506) is now
only known to Celtic storytellers in these islands, but Peele must
have known it in some form. "The King's Daughter of Colchester," or "The Well of the World's End" (Type 408), in
which the three heads appear from the well, is another English
tale with which he was familiar and which was still alive at the
beginning of this century; W. H. Thompson heard a version of
it from an English gypsy, Tommy Smith, in January 1915, and
recorded it in his notebooks. Type 426, "Snow-White and Rose-
Red" (Grimm, No. 161) is unknown to oral tradition in England, but it may have been known there two hundred years

before the Grimm brothers found it in Germany, for the enchanted bear plays an important part in *The Old Wives Tale.*

In *The Knight of the Burning Pestle* (III, iv), the Citizen's Wife speaks of a pretty tale of a witch who had a giant as her son, called Lob-Lie-by-the-Fire. I had imagined that this was a story lost past finding, but in the Archives of The School of Scottish Studies is a tale collected by Hamish Henderson from Bella Stewart of Aberdeen about a very similar creature. In this tale, which begins as a form of Type 1137, a sinister Brownie haunting Fincastle Mill in Perthshire is scalded to death by a girl who is saved from his mother's vengeance by having called herself "Me Myself." Later, however, the witchlike mother, Maggie Moulach, learns the truth and kills the girl. Sinister though this witch is she does real Brownie service at another farm, and the regular Brownie tales are told about her. It is worth noting that Meg Mollach is the name of the female Brownie recorded by Aubrey in *The Remaines of Gentilisme.*

Ben Jonson is another source of folktale references. Among others, he knew a version of Type 1541, the tale of the foolish wife who gave away her husband's savings to a tramp who called himself "Long Winter" or "Good Fortune," or some such name.

The fact that these tales were known in England so early is of more than literary interest. Not only does it give us some notion of the distribution of tale types in the days before general literacy and the publication of folktale collections, but it prepares us to look for these tales, or hints of them, in modern oral tradition. An example I have already cited is Shakespeare's "Mr. Fox." The commonest surviving variants are those of the type of "The Oxford Student" (Halliwell-Phillipps) of which I give the Somerset version, "Mr. Fox's Courtship." One might suppose that this version was the nearest we were now to get, but the T. W. Thompson notebooks contain two, "The Cellar Full of Blood" and "The Hand," which are much nearer to the earlier version. They were collected in 1914.

So much for the wonder tales. They are scarce and fragmentary in England. When we come to legends, or *Sagen*, we are on different ground. The distinction between legends and wonder tales is often a rather nebulous one. Broadly speaking, one may say

that legends are tales or anecdotes told as fact, often about particular places or people, or about friends of the narrator, or his
friends' friends. Thus they are distinguished from other folktales of all kinds, which are told for entertainment or edification,
with only a playful pretense of being factual. This distinction is
clear in the main, but it does not necessarily affect the shape of
the story. Exactly the same story might be told by two men, one
of whom believed it and recorded it as a fact while the other told
it purely as a good tale. A further difficulty is that it seems likely
that legends of the origin of local features—standing stones and
mounds and the like—were never really believed at all, but were
playful exercises of imagination. Many of the Saints' legends,
too, may have been meant for edification rather than history. Yet
these two subdivisions of legend have always been treated as its
very essence. For these reasons I have put the legends next to
the wonder tales in my collection, and not at the end of the book,
as I might have done if I had followed the type index classification of the migratory legends of Reidar Christiansen.

Legends are much more common and more alive in England
than wonder tales. If ghost stories are asked for at a Halloween
or Christmas party an astonishing number of people can tell
really good ones, which are not literary tales but experiences
known in their own families or among their neighbours. Witch
beliefs too have a wider acceptance than many people think.
The modern practitioners of ritual witchcraft may draw more
from literature than tradition, but in country places the traditional witch beliefs are obsolescent, not dead. "The Witch's
Purse," told by Mrs. Falconer, is two generations old by now,
but "Annie Luker's Ghost," heard by Miss Tongue in 1963, is
of very recent occurrence. Even fairy beliefs can still be found,
as a recent broadcast showed. Historical and local legends, too,
are told of almost every village, but the guidebooks have got
hold of most of them, and it is not easy to be sure, in this age of
general literacy, whether the local tales are not a rehashing of the
guidebooks. For this reason I have included only a small number
of the lesser-known local legends, though I have been more
liberal with the historical and quasi-historical traditions. These
are of several kinds. There are the traditional comments on

matters and characters of national importance, such as the loss of King John's jewels and the execution of King Charles I; there are the local repercussions of historical events, such as the Somerset memories of the reign of terror which followed the Monmouth Rebellion, and there are real events of only local importance which yet remain clear in folk memory. Where facts can be historically checked it is of interest to note the increment of legend; that is why I have included "Jack White's Gibbet" among the historical tales. As well as these there are the quasi-historical tales, often international tale types, which are claimed by many places and families as having originally happened to them. Of these tales "The Thievish Sexton" is a representative one.

One kind of legend which has not hitherto received very much attention is the modern legend, investigated by some of the American folklorists. This legend grows up in a more sophisticated society than did the earlier ones, but it has much in common with them. It is related as a true story, and is generally supposed to have happened to a friend of the narrator, or a friend's friend. It is often plausible enough, but it crops up in various places and has slightly different details. Possibly, its source may be a real happening, or a magazine story. A good example is "The Stolen Corpse," several versions of which have been collected by Stewart Sanderson of Leeds University.

Jocular tales have universal currency and proliferate everywhere. These can be placed under all kinds of headings; I have arranged mine according to the specimens I have chosen. One novel and possibly ephemeral type is the shaggy dog story. The absurdities have been with us since the seventeenth-century non sequiturs.

As for the sources of the tales I have chosen, a few are old. It seems fitting to include a tale from John Aubrey, the father of English folklorists. I have chosen one from his Bodleian Wiltshire manuscript; it has never, so far as I know, been published except in the appendix of one of my own books, *Pale Hecate's Team*. After the seventeenth century, the two great periods for English folklore were the beginning and the end of the nineteenth century, or perhaps one should say at the turn of the

nineteenth century. In the earlier of these two periods some valuable material was collected, but it was considered enough for
the collector to be true to the bones of the story; he held himself
free to embellish it with what detail he chose. We must not
despise what was collected then, for it enables us to judge what
tales were known before Grimm and Andersen caught the public
imagination; but we would give much to know the actual words
in which the stories were told. By the end of the nineteenth century, however, when the great folklorists were at work, the importance of verbal accuracy was beginning to be understood,
and Groome, Addy, and Mrs. Balfour give us as nearly as they
can the very words of the narrator. I include a few of these
stories, but the bulk of those in my collection are more modern.

Miss Ruth L. Tongue of Somerset has made so large a con-
tribution to this collection that I have placed her name with
mine on the title page. She is in a curious position as a folktale
collector, because some of her earlier stories may be said to be
collected from herself. Miss Tongue's father was for a time a
chaplain at Taunton Barracks, and in Taunton Miss Tongue
made the acquaintance of the people from whom she learned her
folklore, particularly of a group of old men who used to wash
carts at Taunton Market, and who taught her a large number
of songs. She had one peculiar qualification as a recipient of folk
material not usually confided to a stranger, she was a "chimes
child," that is, she was born between twelve and one on a Friday
and was therefore believed to have the power to see ghosts and
spirits. This admitted her to the confidence of the old people,
not only to the old men of Taunton Market but to a group of
sextons, from whom she learned such traditions and legends as
"The Open Grave." Other sources of many tales were an old
North Somerset groom and the old lady known to her as Annie's
Granny, the grandmother of one of her schoolfellows. Her later
tales were gathered partly because of her knowledge of the earlier
ones, partly because as a horsewoman and a herb doctor she had
earned local respect. She has made a tape recording of her earlier
material, and what has not been tape-recorded has been written
down verbatim from her informants.

I have several times alluded to the T. W. Thompson Notebooks, which are now under the care of Stewart F. Sanderson of the Folk Life Survey of Leeds University. Mr. Thompson is one of the few remaining early members of the Gypsy Lore Society. He collected a number of tales, a few of which have been already published, in the north of England in 1914 and 1915. Some of these tales are only summarized, but they provide most valuable evidence of the survival in English oral tradition of some international tale types not otherwise known in this country. It is to be hoped that the whole collection may soon be published.

Another valuable source of tales is Mr. W. H. Barrett of the Fen country, whose recent books of Fen tales have contributed remarkably to our knowledge of folk life in that once isolated area. Mr. Barrett is now old and almost bedridden, but his intelligence and memory are as strong as ever, and he kindly consented to record some tales for me.

For the rest, the tales are gathered from scattered individuals whom I have to thank for their kindness in recounting them to me. I have also to thank Mr. Basil Megaw and Mr. Hamish Henderson and other members of the School of Scottish Studies whose hospitality allowed me access to their Archives, for very valuable comparison. I am also grateful to Mr. Stewart Sanderson for directing my attention to the Thompson Notebooks and for obtaining permission for me to reproduce "Mossycoat," and to Miss Porter of the Cambridge Folk Museum for first giving me access to Mr. Barrett's papers.

KATHARINE M. BRIGGS

Contents

III. JOCULAR TALES

3

Part I
Wonder Tales

· 1 · *The Small-Tooth Dog*

Collected by Sidney O. Addy in Norton, Derbyshire, and published in his Household Tales with Other Traditional Remains, Collected in the Counties of York, Lincoln, Derby, and Nottingham (*London and Sheffield, 1895*), *No. 1, pp. 1-4. Addy writes in his Introduction: "In every case I have either written the tales down from dictation, or a written copy has been given to me."*

This is Type 425C, Beauty and the Beast, No. 88 in Grimm, and reported throughout Europe. Lithuania leads with 30 versions. Baughman cites examples from Virginia, Massachusetts (Irish informant), New York, North Carolina, and Kentucky.

· ONCE UPON A time, there was a merchant who traveled about the world a great deal. On one of his journeys thieves attacked him, and they would have taken both his life and his money if a large dog had not come to his rescue and driven the thieves away. When the dog had driven the thieves away he took the merchant to his house, which was a very handsome one, and he dressed his wounds and nursed him until he was well.

As soon as he was able to travel the merchant began his journey home, but before starting he told the dog how grateful he was for his kindness, and asked him what reward he could offer in return, and he said he would not refuse to give him the most precious thing that he had.

And so the merchant said to the dog, "Will you accept a fish that I have that can speak twelve languages?"

"No," said the dog, "I will not."

"Or a goose that lays golden eggs?"

"No," said the dog, "I will not."

"Or a mirror in which you can see what anybody is thinking about?"

"No," said the dog, "I will not."

"Then what will you have?" said the merchant.

"I will have none of such presents," said the dog, "but let me fetch your daughter, and take her to my house."

When the merchant heard this he was grieved, but what he had promised had to be done, so he said to the dog, "You can come and fetch my daughter after I have been at home for a week."

So at the end of the week the dog came to the merchant's house to fetch his daughter, but when he got there he stayed outside the door, and would not go in. But the merchant's daughter did as her father told her, and came out of the house dressed for a journey and ready to go with the dog.

When the dog saw her he looked pleased, and said, "Jump on my back, and I will take you away to my house." So she mounted on the dog's back, and away they went at a great pace until they reached the dog's house, which was many miles off.

But after she had been a month at the dog's house she began to mope and cry.

"What are you crying for?" said the dog.

"Because I want to go back to my father," she said.

The dog said, "If you will promise me that you will not stay at home more than three days I will take you there. But first of all," said he, "what do you call me?"

"A great, foul, small-tooth dog," said she.

"Then," said he, "I will not let you go."

But she cried so pitifully that he promised again to take her home. "But before we start," said he, "tell me what you call me."

"Oh!" said she, "your name is Sweet-as-a-honeycomb."

"Jump on my back," said he, "and I'll take you home." So he trotted away with her on his back for forty miles, when they came to a stile.

"And what do you call me?" said he, before they got over the stile.

Thinking that she was safe on her way, the girl said, "A great, foul, small-tooth dog." But when she said this, he did not jump over the stile, but turned right round about at once, and galloped back to his own house with the girl on his back.

Another week went by, and again the girl wept so bitterly that the dog promised to take her to her father's house. So the girl got on the dog's back again, and they reached the first stile as before, and then the dog stopped and said, "And what do you call me?"

"Sweet-as-a-honeycomb," she replied.

So the dog leaped over the stile, and they went on for twenty miles until they came to another stile.

"And what do you call me?" said the dog, with a wag of his tail.

She was thinking more of her own father and her own home than of the dog, so she answered, "A great, foul, small-tooth dog."

Then the dog was in a great rage, and he turned right round about and galloped back to his own house as before. After she had cried for another week, the dog promised again to take her back to her father's house. So she mounted upon his back once more, and when they got to the first stile, the dog said, "And what do you call me?"

"Sweet-as-a-honeycomb," she said.

So the dog jumped over the stile, and away they went—for now the girl made up her mind to say the most loving things she could think of—until they reached her father's house.

When they got to the door of the merchant's house, the dog said, "And what do you call me?"

Just at that moment the girl forgot the loving things that she meant to say, and began, "A great..." but the dog began to turn, and she got fast hold of the door-latch, and was going to say "foul," when she saw how grieved the dog looked and remembered how good and patient he had been with her, so she said, "Sweeter-than-a-honeycomb."

When she had said this she thought the dog would have been content and have galloped away, but instead of that he suddenly stood up on his hind legs, and with his fore legs he pulled off his dog's head, and tossed it high in the air. His hairy coat dropped off, and there stood the handsomest young man in the world, with the finest and smallest teeth you ever saw.

Of course they were married, and lived together happily.

·2· *The Green Lady*

Printed by Alice B. Gomme in Folk-Lore, *VII (1896), 411–14,
"The Green Lady: A Folktale from Hertfordshire." Lady
Gomme heard the tale as a child from her nursemaid, Mary
Ann Smith, who forgot some of the rhymes.*

*The story contains episodes I, V, VI, and VII from a celebrated
international tale, Type 480,* The Spinning-Women by the
Spring. The Kind and the Unkind Girls. *In Grimms'* Household
Tales *it is No. 24, "Frau Holle." A full-length study has been
published by Warren E. Roberts,* The Tale of the Kind and Unkind Girls *(Berlin, 1958), which examines over nine hundred
versions. The distribution is densest in northern Europe, with
Finland, Estonia, and Sweden each reporting over one hundred
texts. It is well known in India;* Folktales of Japan, *a companion
volume in this series, gives three examples (Nos. 33, 34, 35).*

*Baughman lists several shorter or longer English variants of
Type 480: Addy,* Household Tales, *No. 10, "The Little Water-
cress Girl," and No. 18, "The Glass Ball"; Henderson,* Northern
Counties *(1879 ed.), pp. 349–50; Grice,* North Country, *"The
Ji-Jaller Bag," pp. 108–10. Hartland gives an 1823 chapbook
version in* English Fairy and other Folk Tales, *"The Princess of
Colchester," pp. 20–24, reprinted by Jacobs in* English Fairy
Tales, *pp. 232–37. A cante-fable text from Kentucky is re-
printed in R. M. Dorson,* Buying the Wind *(Chicago, 1964),
pp. 206–209.*

*Common motifs include G204, "Girl in service of witch";
Q42.1.1, "Child divides last loaf with fairy (witch, etc.)";
D1821.3.6, "Magic sight by looking through keyhole"; B470.1,
"Small fish as helper"; and Q2, "Kind and unkind."*

• ONCE UPON A time, there was an old man who had two daughters. Now one of these girls was a steady, decent girl, and the
other was a stuck-up, proud, conceited piece; but the father liked

her best, and she had the most to eat, and the best clothes to wear.

One day, the nice girl said to her father, "Father, give me a cake and a bottle of beer, and let me go and seek my fortune."

So the father gave her a cake and a bottle of beer, and she went out to seek her fortune. After she had walked a weary while through the wood, she sat down by a tree to rest herself, and eat her cake and drink her beer. While she was eating, a little old man came by, and he said, "Little girl, little girl, what are you doing under my tree?"

She said, "I am going to seek my fortune, sir; I am very tired and hungry, and I am eating my dinner."

The old man said, "Little girl, little girl, give me some dinner too."

She said, "I have only a cake and a bottle of beer; if you like to have some of that, you may."

The old man said he would; so he sat down and they ate the cake, and drank the beer all up. Then the little girl was going on further, and the old man said: "I will tell you where to seek your fortune. Go on further and further into the wood, until you come to a little old cottage, where the Green Lady lives. Knock at the door and when she opens it, tell her you've come to seek service. She will take you in; mind you be a good girl, and do all she tells you to do, and you'll come to no harm."

So the little girl thanked him kindly and went on her way. Presently she came to the little cottage in the wood, and she knocked at the door. Then the door was opened by a pretty Green Lady, who said, "Little girl, little girl, what do you want?"

"I've come to seek service, ma'am," said the little girl.

"What can you do?" asked the Green Lady.

"I can bake and I can brew, and about the house all things can do," said the little girl.

"Then come in," said the Green Lady, and she took her into the kitchen. "Now," said she, "you must be a very good girl; sweep the house well; make the dust fly; and mind you don't look through the keyhole, or harm will befall you."

The little girl swept the house and made the dust fly.

Then the Green Lady said, "Now, go to the well, and bring
in a pail of nice clean water to cook the supper in. If the water
isn't clean, change it and change it till it is."

Then the little girl took a pail and went to the well. The first
pail she drew, the water was so muddy and dirty, she threw it
away. The next pailful she drew, the water was a little clearer,
but there was a silver fish in it.

The fish said, "Little girl, little girl, wash me and comb me,
and lay me down softly."

So she washed it and combed it, and laid it down softly. Then
she drew another pailful. The water was a little clearer, but
there was a gold fish in it.

The fish said, "Little girl, little girl, wash me and comb me,
and lay me down softly."

So she washed it and combed it, and laid it down softly. Then
she drew another pailful. There was clear water, but there was
still another fish who said the same thing as the others; so she
washed this one too, combed it, and laid it down softly. Then
she drew another pailful, and this was quite fresh and clear.

Then the three fish raised their heads and said:

> They who eat the fairies' food
> In the churchyard soon shall dwell.
> Drink the water of this well,
> And all things for thee shall be good.
> Be but honest, bold and true,
> So shall good fortune come to you.

Then the little girl hasted to the house, swept up the kitchen,
and made the dust fly quickly, for she thought she would surely
be scolded for being away so long, and she was hungry too. The
Green Lady then showed her how to cook the supper, and take
it into the parlor, and told her she could take some bread and
milk for herself afterwards. But the little girl said she would
rather have a drink of water and some of her own cake; she
had found some crumbs in her pocket you must know. Then the
Green Lady went into the parlor, and the little girl sat down by
the fire. Then she was thinking about her place, and what the
fish had said, and she wondered why the Green Lady had told

her not to look through the keyhole. She thought there could not be any harm in doing this, and she looked through the keyhole, when what should she see but the Green Lady dancing with a bogey! She was so surprised that she called out:

> "Oh! what can I see?
> A green lady dancing with a bogey."

The Green Lady rushed out of the room and said: "What can you see?"

The little girl replied,

> "Nothing can I see, nothing can I spy,
> Nothing can I see till the days high die."
> [The day I die?]

Then the Green Lady went into the parlor again to have her supper, and the little girl again looked through the keyhole. Again she sang:

> "Oh! what can I see?
> A green lady dancing with a bogey."

The Green Lady rushed out: "Little girl, little girl, what can you see?"

The girl said,

> "Nothing can I see, nothing can I spy,
> Nothing can I see till the days high die."

This happened a third time, and then the Green Lady said: "Now you shall see no more," and she blinded the little girl's eyes. "But," said the Green Lady, "because you have been a good girl, and made the dust fly, I will give you your wages and you shall go home."

So she gave her a bag of money and a bundle of clothes, and sent her away. So the little girl stumbled along the path in the dark and presently she stumbled against the well. Now, there was a fine young man sitting on the edge of the well, and he told her he had been sent by the fish of the well to see her home, and would carry her bag of money and her bundle for her. He told her, too, before starting on her journey, to bathe her eyes in the well. [Rhyme missing here.] This she did and she found her eyes come back to her, and she could see as well as ever. So the young man and the little girl went along together, until they arrived at her father's cottage; and when the bag was opened, there was all sorts of money in it, and when the bundle was opened, there was all sorts of fine clothes in it. And the little girl married the young man, and they lived happy ever after.

Now, when the other girl saw all the fine things her sister had got, she came to her father and said, "Father, give me a cake and a bottle of beer, and let me seek my fortune."

Her father gave her a cake and a bottle of beer, and the same things happened to her as to her sister. But when the old man asked her for some dinner, she said, "I haven't enough for myself; so I can't give you any," and when she was at the Green Lady's house, she didn't make the dust fly, and the Green Lady was cross with her; and when she went to the well and the fish got into her pails of water, she said the fishes were wet, sloppy things, and she wasn't going to mess her hands and clean frock with them, and she threw them back roughly into the well; and she said she wasn't going to drink nasty cold water for her supper, when she could have nice bread and milk; and when the Green Lady put her eyes out for looking through the keyhole, she didn't get a bag of money and a bundle of clothes or her wages, because she hadn't made the dust fly, and she had no one to help her and take her home. So she wandered about all night and all day, and she died; and no one knows where she was buried or what became of her.

•3• *Tom Tit Tot*

Reprinted by Edward Clodd in "The Philosophy of Rumpelstilt-skin," Folk-Lore Journal, VII (1889), 138–43, from the Ipswich Journal, Notes and Queries, edited by the noted collector of gipsy folktales, F. Hindes Groome, who received the tale from a lady who had heard it in childhood from a West Suffolk nurse.

Clodd was fascinated by this folktale as an example of survival

*from the savage belief of magic in names, and developed his
study into a full-length book,* Tom Tit Tot, An Essay on Savage
Philosophy in Folk-Tale (*London, 1898*). *The most famous version is Grimm No. 55,* "Rumpelstilzchen." *This story is Type 500,*
The Name of the Helper, *most heavily reported in Ireland, Germany, Denmark, and Finland. Key motifs are H521, "Test:
guessing unknown propounder's name"; H1092, "Tasks: spin-
ning impossible amount in one night"; and N475, "Secret name
overheard by eavesdropper."*

In England, a long Cornish droll was printed by Robert Hunt
in Popular Romances from the West of England, First Series
(London, 1865), pp. 273–84, under the title "Duffy and the
Devil." Hartland reprinted the present text in English Fairy and
Other Folk Tales, pp. 28–34. Robert Chambers gives a Scottish
text in The Popular Rhymes of Scotland, pp. 262–63. An
American Negro text from North Carolina is in the Journal of
American Folklore, XXX (1917), 198. Three versions of Type
500 appear in Folktales of Norway, a companion volume in this
series, Nos. 5, 7, and 159.

The present text is told in West Suffolk dialect. "Maw'r" or
"Mawther" is the curious Suffolk word for a daughter or young
maid. "Gatless" means heedless or senseless.

• WELL, ONCE UPON a time, there were a woman and she baked
five pies. And when they come out of the oven, they was that
overbaked, the crust were too hard to eat. So she says to her
darter—

"Maw'r," she says, "put you them there pies on the shelf an'
leave 'em there a little, an' they'll come agin,"—she meant, you
know, the crust 'ud get soft.

But the gal, she says to herself, "Well, if they'll come agin,
I'll ate 'em now." And she set to work and ate 'em all, first and
last.

Well, come supper time, the woman she said, "Goo you and
git one o' them there pies. I daresay they've come agin now."

The gal she went an' she looked, and there worn't nothin' but
the dishes. So back she come and says she, "Noo, they ain't
come agin."

"Not none on 'em?" says the mother.

"Not none on 'em," says she.

"Well, come agin or not come agin," says the woman, "I'll ha' one for supper."

"But you can't, if they ain't come," says the gal.

"But I can," says she. "Goo you and bring the best of 'em."

"Best or worst," says the gal, "I've ate 'em all, and you can't ha' one till that's come agin."

Well, the woman she were wholly bate, and she took her spinnin' to the door, to spin, and as she span she sang—

> "My darter ha' ate five, five pies today—
> My darter ha' ate five, five pies today."

The king he were a-comin' down the street an' he hard her sing but what she sang he couldn't hare, so he stopped and said—

"What were that you was a-singun of, maw'r?"

The woman she were ashamed to let him hare what her darter had been a'doin', so she sang 'stids o' that—

> "My darter ha' spun five, five skeins today—
> My darter ha' spun five, five skeins today."

"S'ars o' mine!" says the king, "I never heerd tell o' anyone as could do that."

Then he said, "Look you here, I want a wife, an' I'll marry your darter. But look you here," says he, " 'leven months out o' the year, she shall have all the vittles she likes to eat, and all the gownds she likes to git, and all the cumpny she likes to hev; but the last month o' the year she'll ha' to spin five skeins iv'ry day, an' if she doon't I shall kill her."

"All right," says the woman; for she thowt that was a grand marriage that was. And as for them five skeins, when te come tew, there'd be plenty o' ways o' getting out of it and likeliest he'd ha' forgot about it.

Well, so they was married. An' for 'leven months the gal had all the vittles she liked to ate, and all the gownds she liked to git, and all the cumpny she liked to hev.

But when the time was gettin' oover, she began to think about them there skeins, an' to wonder if he had 'em in mind. But not one word did he say about 'em, and she whoolly thowt he'd forgot about 'em.

Howsiver, the last day o' the last month, he takes her to a room she'd niver set eyes on afore. There worn't nothin' in it but a spinnin' wheel and a stool. An' says he, "Now, me dear, hare yow'll be shut in tomorrow, with some vittles and some flax, and if you hain't spun five skeins by the night, yar hid'll goo off."

An' awa he went about his business.

Well, she were that frightened. She'd allus been such a gatless mawther, that she didn't se much as know how to spin, an' what were she to dew tomorrer with no one to come nigh her to help her. She sat down on a stool in the kitchen, and lork! how she did cry!

Howsiver, all on a sudden, she hard a sort of a knockin' low down on the door. She upped and oped it, an' what should she see but a small, little black thing with a long tail. That looked up at her right kewrious, an' that said:

"What are yew a-crying for?"

"Wha's that to yew?" says she.

"Niver yew mind," that said, "but tell me what yew're a-crying for."

"That don't dew me no good if I dew," says she.

"Yew doon't know that," that said, an' twirled that's tail round.

"Well," says she, "that oon't dew no harm, if that doon't dew no good," and she upped and told about the pies an' the skeins an' everything.

"This is what I'll dew," says the little black thing. "I'll come to yar winder iv'ry mornin', an' take the flax an' bring it spun at night."

"Wha's your pay?" says she.

That looked out o' the corners o' that's eyes, an' that said: "I'll give you three guesses every night to guess my name, an' if you hain't guessed it afore the month's up, yew shall be mine."

Well, she thowt she'd be sure to guess that's name afore the month was up. "All right," says she, "I agree."

"All right," that says, and lork! how that twirled that's tail.

Well, the next day her husband he took her inter the room, an' there was the flax an' the day's vittles.

"Now, there's the flax," says he, "an' if that ain't spun up this night, off goo yar hid." An' then he went out an' locked the door.

He'd hardly goon, when there was a knockin' agin the winder. She upped and oped it, and there, sure enough, were the little oo'd thing a-settin' on the ledge.

"Where's the flax?" says he.

"Here te be," says she. And she gonned it to him.

Well, come the evenin', a knockin' come agin to the winder. She upped an' oped it, and there were the little oo'd thing, with five skeins of flax on his arm.

"Here te be," says he, an' he gonned it to her. "Now, what's my name?" says he.

"What, is that Bill?" says she.

"Noo, that ain't," says he. An' he twirled his tail.

"Is that Ned?" says she.

"Noo, that ain't," says he. An' he twirled his tail.

"Well, is that Mark?" says she.

"Noo, that ain't," says he. An' he twirled his tail harder, an' awa' he flew.

Well, when her husban' he come in, there was the five skeins riddy for him. "I see as I shorn't hev to kill you tonight, me dare," says he. "Yew'll hev yar vittles, and yar flax in the mornin'," says he, an' away he goes.

Well, ivery day the flax an' the vittles, they was browt, an' ivery day that there little black impet used for to come mornin's an' evenin's.

An' all the day the mawther she set a-tryin' fur to think of names to say to it when te come at night. But she nivver hot on the right one. An' as that got to-warts the ind o' the month, the impet that began for to look soo maliceful, an' that twirled that's tail faster an' faster, each time she gave a guess.

At last te come to the last day but one. The impet that come at night along o' the five skeins, an' that said,

"What, hain't yew got my name yet?"

"Is that Nicodemus?" says she.

"Noo, t'ain't," that says.

"Is that Sammle?" says she.

"Noo, t'ain't," that says.

"A-well, is that Methusalem?" says she.

"Noo, t'ain't that norther," he says.

Then that looks at her with that's eyes like a cool o' fire, an' that says, "Woman, there's only tomorrer night, an' then yar'll be mine." An' awa' he flew.

Well, she felt that horrud. Howsomediver, she hard the king a-comin' along the passage.

In he came, an' when he sees the five skeins, he says, says he, "Well, me dare," says he, "I don't see but what yew'll ha' your skeins ready tomorrer night as well, an' as I reckon I shorn't ha' to kill you, I'll ha' supper in here tonight." So they brought supper, an' another stool for him, and down the tew they sat.

Well, he hadn't eat but a mouthful or so, when he stops an' begins to laugh.

"What is it?" says she.

"A-why," says he, "I was out a-huntin' today, an' I got away to a place in the wood I'd never seen afore. An' there was an old chalk pit. An' I heerd a sort of a hummin', kind o'. So I got off my hobby, an' I went right quiet to the pit, an' I looked down. Well, what should there be but the funniest little black thing yew iver set eyes on. An' what was that a-dewin' on, but that had a little spinnin' wheel, an' that were a-spinnin' wonner- ful fast, an' a-twirlin' that's tail. An' as that span, that sang,

> Nimmy nimmy not,
> My name's Tom Tit Tot.

Well, when the mawther heerd this, she fared as if she could a jumped outer her skin for joy, but she din't say a word.

Next day, that there little thing looked soo maliceful when he come for the flax. An' when night came, she heerd that a-knockin' agin the winder panes. She oped the winder, an' that come right in on the ledge. That were grinning from are to are, an' oo! tha's tail were twirlin' round so fast.

"What's my name?" that says, as that gonned her the skeins.

4

"Is that Solomon?" she says, pretendin' to be afeard.

"Noo, t'ain't," that says, an' that come fudder inter the room.

"Well, is that Zebedee?" says she agin.

"Noo, t'aint," says the impet. An' then that laughed an' twirled that's tail till yew cou'n't hardly see it.

"Take time, woman," that says, "next guess, an' yew're mine." An' that stretched out that's black hands at her.

Well, she backed a step or two, an' she looked at it, an' then she laughed out, an' says she, a-pointin' of her finger at it,

> Nimmy nimmy not,
> Yar name's Tom Tit Tot.

Well, when that hard her, that shruck awful, an' awa' that flew, into the dark, an' she niver saw it noo more.

•4• *Mossycoat*

Collected by T. W. Thompson from Taimie Boswell, a gipsy, at Oswaldwhistle, Northumberland, January 9, 1915. Published from the T. W. Thompson manuscript collection by permission of the Director of the University of Leeds Folk Life Survey.

This is Type 510B, The Dress of Gold, of Silver, and of Stone, *a form of Cinderella. In England it is well known as "The Story of Catskin"; see the rhymed version in James Orchard Halliwell-Phillipps,* The Nursery Rhymes of England *(London, 1843), pp. 10–15. But there are important variations to note in the present text. In the first place, it is colored by the traveling man's outlook. It is the technique of gipsies and tinkers to go to the front door, and try to see the mistress of the house. They have a rooted distrust of servants and underlings. In many versions of the tale, it is the young master who ill-treats the heroine, and not the servants. The unnatural love of the father is left out of this tale, and Mossycoat is courted by a peddler. In many variants, the magic powers are bestowed by the dead mother; Boswell's text is unusual in that the mother is still alive, though she disappears from the story as soon as the magic petticoat has been given. In one variant, the heroine is dressed in a wooden gown, which becomes covered with moss. Otherwise, "Mossycoat" is unique.*

Type 510B is practically world-wide in distribution, save for the Far East. English texts are printed by Andrew Lang, Folk-Lore, I *(1890), "Cap o' Rushes," 295–99; Eveline C. Gurdon,* County Folk-Lore No. 1 *(London, 1893), "Folk-Lore of Suffolk," pp. 40–43; Joseph Jacobs,* More English Fairy Tales, *"Catskin," pp. 62–72, 204–10. In the United States, examples are known from the southern Appalachians and the Schoharie Hills, New York (see references in Baughman,* England and North America*).*

A version of the related form, Type 510A, is printed in Folktales of Japan, *a companion volume in this series, No. 38, "Benizara and Kakezara." Motifs present are D1470.1, "Magic wishing object causes wishes to be fulfilled"; F821.1.5, "Dress of gold, silver, color of sun, moon, and stars"; H36.1, "Slipper test"; L162, "Lowly heroine marries prince"; N711.6, "Prince sees heroine at ball and is enamoured"; and R221, "Heroine's three-fold flight from ball."*

• DERE WAS ONCE a poor ould widder-woman as lived in a little cottage. She'd two daughters; de younger on 'em was about nineteen or twenty, and she was very beautiful. Her mother was busy ivry day, a-spinning of a coat for her.

A hawker came courting dis girl; came reg'lar he did, and kept on a-bringing of her dis thing and dat. He was in love wid her, and badly wanted her to marry him. But she wasn't in love wid him; it didn't fall out like dat; and she was in a puzzlement what she'd best do about him. So one day she ext her mother. "Let he come," her mother telt her, "and git what you can out'n him, while I finish dis coat, after when you won't have no need 'n him, nor his presents neether. So tell him, girl, as you won't marry him, unless he gits you a dress o' white satin with sprigs o' goold on it as big as a man's hand; and mind as you tells him it mus' fit exac'ly."

Next time de hawker cam round, and ext her to wed him, de girl telt him just dis, de wery same as her mother'd said. He took stock 'n her size and build, de hawker did; and inside of a week he was back wid de dress. It answered de describance all right, an when de girl went upstairs wid her mother, and tried it on, it fit 'n exac'ly.

"What should I do now, Mother?" she ext.

"Tell him," her mother says, "as you won't marry him unless he gits you a dress med o' silk de color o' all de birds o' de air; and as afore, it must fit you exac'ly."

De girl telt de hawker dis, and in two or three days he was back at de cottage, wid dis colored silk dress de girl ed exted for; and being as he knowed de size from de t'other un, in course it fit her exac'ly.

"Now what should I do, Mother?" she ext. "Tell him," her mother says, "as you won't marry him unless he gits you a pair o' silver slippers as fits you exac'ly." De girl telt de hawker so, and in a few days he called round wid 'em. Her feet was only about three inches long, but de slippers fit her exac'ly; dey was not too tight, neether was dey too loose. Agen de girl ext her mother what she should do now. "I can finish de coat tonight," her mother said, "so you can tell de hawker as you'll marry him tomorrow, and he's to be here at 10 o'clock." So de girl telt him dis. "Think-on, my dear," she says, "10 o'clock in de morning." "I'll be dere, my love," he says, "by God, I will."

That night her mother was at work on de coat till late, but she finished it all right. Green moss and goold thread, dat's what it was med on; just dem two things. "Mossycoat," she called it, and give de name to de younger daughter, as she'd med it for. It was a magic coat, she said, a wishing coat, she telt her daughter; when she'd got it on, she telt her she'd only to wish to be somewhere, and she'd be dere dat wery instant, and de same if she wanted to change hersel' into summat else, like to be a swan or a bee.

Next morning de mother was up by it was light. She called her younger daughter, and telt her she mus' now go into de world and seek her fortune, and a handsome fortune it was to be. She was a foreseer, de owld mother was, and know'd what was a-coming. She give her daughter mossycoat to put on, and a goold crown to tek wid her, and she telt her to tek as well de two dresses and de silver slippers she'd had off'n de hawker. But she was to go in de clo'es as she wore ivery day, her working clo'es dat is. And now she's ready for to start, Mossycoat is. Her mother den tells her she is to wish herself a hundred miles away, and den walk on till she comes to a big hall, and dere she's to ext for a job. "You won't hev far to walk, my blessed," she says —dat's de mother. "And dey'll be sure to find you work at dis big hall."

Mossycoat did as her mother telt her, and soon she foun' herself in front of a big gentleman's house. She knocked at de front door and said as she was looking for work. Well, de long and de short of it was as de mistress hersel' come to see her; and she liked de look 'n her, de lady did.

"What work can you do?" she ext.

"I can cook, your ladyship," said Mossycoat. "In fact, I'm in de way o' being a wery good cook, from what peoples 'es remarked."

"I can't give you a job as cook," de lady tells her, "being as I got one already; but I'd be willing to imploy you to help de cook, if so as you'd be satisfied wid dat."

"Thank you, ma'am," says Mossycoat. "I s'd be real glad 'n de place."

So it was settled as she was to be undercook. And after when de lady'd showed her up to her bedroom, she took her to de kitchen, and interdoosed her to de t'other sarvants.

"Dis is Mossycoat," she tells 'em, "and I've ingaged her," she says, "to be undercook."

She leaves 'em den, de mistress does; and Mossycoat she goes up to her bedroom agen, to unpack her things, and hide away her goold crown and silver slippers, and her silk and satin dresses.

It goes wi'out saying as de t'other kitchen girls was fair beside theirsels wid jealousy; and it didn't mend matters as de new girl was a dam' sight beautifuller nor what any of dem was. Here was dis wagrant i' rags put above dem, when all she was fit for at best was to be scullery girl. If anybody was to be undercook, it stands to sense it sud 'er been one o' dem as really knowed about things, not dis girl i' rags and tatters, picked up off'n de roads. But dey'd put her in her place, dey would. So dey goes on and on, like what women will, till Mossycoat come down ready to start work. Den dey sets on her. "Who de devil did she think she was, setting hersel' above dem? She'd be under-cook, would she? No dam' fear . . . dey relow of dat. What she'd hev to do, and all she was fit for, was to scour de pans, clean de knives, do de grates and suchlike; and all she'd git was dis." And down come de skimmer on top of her head, pop, pop, pop. "Dat's what you deserves," dey tell her, "and dat's what you can expect, my lady."

And dat's how it was wid Mossycoat. She was put to do all de dirtiest work, and soon she was up to de ears in grease, and her face as black as soot. And ivery now and agen, first one and then another o' de sarvants 'ld pop, pop, pop her a-top o' de head wid de skimmer, till de poor girl's head was dat sore, she couldn't hardly bide it.

Well, it got on, and it got on, and still Mossycoat was at her pans, and knives, and grates; and still de sarvants was pop, pop, popping her on de head wid de skimmer. Now dere was a big dance coming on, as was to last three nights, wid hunting and other sports in de daytime. All de headmost people for miles round was to be dere; and de master, and mistress, and de young master—dey'd niver had but one child—in course dey was a-going. It was all de talk among de sarvants, dis dance was. One was wishing she could be dere; another 'd like to dance wid some 'n de young lords; a third 'ld like to see de ladies' dresses, and so dey went on, all excepting Mossycoat. If only dey'd de clo'es, dey'd be al right, dey thought, as dey considered deirselves as good as high-titled ladies any day. "And you, Mossycoat, you'd like to go, wouldn't you now?" dey says. "A fit person you'd be to be dere in all your rags and dirt," dey says, and down comes de skimmer on her head, pop, pop, pop. Den dey laughs at her; which goes to show what a low class o' people dey was.

Now Mossycoat, as I've said afore, was wery handsome, and rags and dirt couldn't hide dat. De t'other sarvants might think as it did, but de young master'd hed his eyes on her, and de master and mistress, dey'd al'ays taken partic'lar notice o' her,

on account of her good looks. When de big dance was coming
on, dey thought as it'd be nice to ex her to go to it; so dey sent
for her to see if she'd like to. "No, thank you," she says, "I'd
niver think o' such a thing. I knows my place better'n dat," she
says. "Besides, I'd greasy all de one side o' de coach," she tells
'em, "and anybody's clo'es as I comed up agen." Dey make light
on dat, and presses her to go, de master and mistress does. It's
wery kind on 'em, Mossycoat says, but she's not for going, she
says. And she sticks to dat. When she gets back into de kitchen,
you may depend on it, de t'other sarvants wants to know why
she'd bin sent for. Had she got notice, or what was it? So she telt
'em de master and mistress 'ed ext her would she like to go to the
dance wid 'em. "What? You?" dey says, "it's unbelievable. If it
had been one o' we, now, dat'd be different. But you! Why,
you'd niver be relowed in, as you'd greasy all the gentlemen's
clo'es, if dere were any as 'ed dance wid a scullery girl; and de
ladies, dey'd be forced to howld dere noses w'en dey passed by
you, to be sure dey would." No, dey couldn't believe, dey said,
as de master and mistress had iver ext *her* to go to de ball wid
'em. She must be lying, dey said, and down come de skimmer
a-top of her head, pop, pop, pop.

Next night, de master and de mistress and dere son, dis time,
ext her to go to de dance. It was a grand affair de night before,
dey said, and she sud ev bin dere. It was going to be still grander
tonight, dey said, and dey begged of her to come wid 'em,
especially de young master. But no, she says, on account of her
rags and her grease, and dirt, she couldn't, and she wouldn't;
and even de young master couldn't persuade her, though it wasn't
for de want o' trying. The t'other sarvants just didn't believe her
when she telt 'em about her being invited agen to de dance, and
about de young master being wery pressing.

"Hark to her!" they says, "What'll de upstart say next? And
all dam' lies," dey says. Den one o' dem, wid a mouth like a pig-
trough, and legs like a cart horse, catches hold o' de skimmer,
and down it comes, pop, pop, pop, on Mossycoat's head.

Dat night, Mossycoat decided as she'd go to de dance, in right
proper style, all on her own, and wi'out nobody knowing it. De
first thing she does is to put all de t'other sarvants into a trance;

she just touches each on 'em, unnoticed, as she moves about, and
dey all falls asleep under a spell as soon as she does, and can't
wake up agen on deir own; de spell has to be broke by somebody
wid de power, same as she has through her magic coat, or has got
it some other way. Next Mossycoat has a real good wash: she'd
niver been relowed to afore, sin' she'd bin at de hall as the other
sarvants was retermined to mek and to keep her as greasy and
dirty as dey could. Den she goes upstairs to her bedroom, throws
off her working clo'es and shoes, and puts on her white satin
dress wid de gowld sprigs, her silver slippers, and her gowld
crown. In course, she had mossy coat on underneath. So as soon
as she was ready, she jus' wished hersel' at de dance, and dere
she was, wery near as soon as de wish was spoke. She did jus' feel
hersel' rising up and flying through de elements but only for a
moment. Den she was in de ballroom.

De young master sees her standing dere, and once he catched
sight on her he can't tek his eyes off her; he'd niver seen anybody
as han'some afore, or as beautifully dressed. "Who is she?" he
exes his mother; but she doesn't know, she tells him.

"Can't you find out, Mother?" he says, "Can't you go and talk
to her?" His mother sees as he'll niver rest till she does, so she
goes and interdooses hersel' to de young lady, and exes her who
she is, where she comes from, and such as dat; but all she could
git out 'n her was as she come from a place where dey hit her on
de head wid de skimmer. Den presently, de young master he
goes over and interdooses hissel', but she doesn't tell him her
name nor nothing; and when he exes her to hev a dance wid him,
she says no, she'd rather not. He stops aside of her though, and
keeps exing her time and agen, and at de finish she says as she
will, and links up wid him. Dey dances once, up and down de
room; den she says she must go. He presses her to stop, but it's
a waste o' breath; she's retermined to go, dere and den.

"All right," he says—dere was nothing else he could say—
"I'll come and see you off." But she jus' wished she was at home,
and dere she was. No seeing of her off for de young master,
dere warn't, she jus' went from his side in de twinkle of an eye,
leaving him standing dere gaping wid wonderment. Thinking
she might be in de hall, or de porch, a-waiting of her carriage,

he goes to see, but dere's no sign on her anywheres inside or out, and nobody as he exed seen her go. He went back to de ball-room, but he can't think of nothing or nobody but her and all de time he's a-wanting to go home.

When Mossycoat gets back home, she meks sure as all de t'other sarvants is still in a trance. Den she goes up and changes into her working get-up; and after when she'd done dat, she come down into de kitchen agen, and touches each 'n de sarvants. Dat wakens 'em, as you might say; anyway, dey starts up, wondering whatever time o' day it is, and how long dey bin asleep. Mossycoat tells 'em, and drops a hint as she may have to let de mistress know. Dey begs on her not to let on about 'em, and most'n 'em thinks to give her things if she won't. Owld things, dey was, but wid a bit o' wear in 'em still—a skirt, a pair o' shoes, stockings, stays, and what not. So Mossycoat promises as she won't tell on 'em. An' dat night, dey don't hit her on de head wid de skimmer.

All next day de young master is unrestful. He can't settle his mind to nothing but de young lady as he'd fell in love wid last night at de wery first sight 'n her. He was wondering all de time would she be dere agen tonight, and would she vanish de same as she done last night; and thinking how he could stop her, or catch up wid her if she was for doing dis a second time. He must find out where she lives, he thinks, else how's he to go on after when de dance is over. He'd die, he tells his mother, if he can't git her for his wife; he's dat madly in love wid her. "Well," says his mother, "I thought as she was a nice modest girl, but she wouldn't say who or what she was, or where she come from, except it was a place where dey hit her on de head wid de skimmer."

"She's a bit of a mystery, I know," says de young master, "but dat don't signify as I want her any de less. I must hev her, Mother," he says, "whoiver and whativer she is; and dat's de dear God's truth, Mother, strike me dead if it ain't."

Women sarvants 'es long ears, and big mouths, and you may be sure as it wasn't long afore de young master and dis wonder-ful han'some lady he'd fell in love wid was all de talk in de kitchen.

"And fancy you, Mossycoat, thinking as he specially wanted *you* to go to de dance," dey says, and starts in on her proper, meking all manner o' nasty sarcastical remarks, and hitting her on de head wid de skimmer, pop, pop, pop, for lying to 'em (as dey said). It was de same agen later on, after when de master and mistress hed sent for her, and exed her once more to go to de dance wid 'em, and once more she'd defused. It was her last chance, dey said—dat was de sarvants—an' a lot more besides, as ain't worth repeating. And down came de skimmer a-top of her head, pop, pop, pop. Den she put de whole devil's breed 'n 'em into a trance like she done de night afore, and got hersel' ready to go to de dance, de only difference being as dis time she put her t'other dress on, de one med o' silk de color of all de birds o' de air.

She's in de ballroom now, Mossycoat is. De young master, he's waiting and watching for her. As soon as he sees her, he exes his father to send for de fastest horse in his stable, and hev it kept standing ready saddled at de door. Den he exes his mother to go over and talk to de young lady for a bit. She does dat, but can't larn no more about her 'an she did the night afore. Den de young master hears as his horse is ready at de door; so he goes over to de young lady, and exes her for a dance. She says jus' de same as de night afore, "No," at first, but "Yes," at de finish, and jus' as den, she says she mus' go after when dey've danced only once de length o' de room an' back. But dis time, he keeps howld 'n her till dey gets outside. Den she wishes hersel' at home, and is dere nearly as soon as she's spoken. De young master felt her rise into de air, but couldn't do nothing to stop her. But p'raps he did jus' touch her foot, as she dropped one slipper; I couldn't be sure as he did; it looks a bit like it though. He picks de slipper up; but as for catching up wid her, it would be easier by far to catch up wid de wind on a blowy night. As soon as she gits home, Mossycoat changes back into her owld things; den she looses de t'other sarvants from de spell she'd put on 'em. Dey've been asleep agen, dey thinks, and offers her one a shilling, another a half a crown, a third a week's wage, if she won't tell on 'em; and she promises as she won't.

De young master's in bed next day, a-dying for de love of de lady as lost one 'n her silver slippers de night afore. De doctors can't do him not de leastest good. So it was give out what his state was, and as it was only de lady able to wear de slipper as could save his life; and if she'd come forrad, he'd marry her. De slippers, as I said earlier on, was only but three inches long, or dereabouts. Ladies came from near and far, some wid big feet and some wid small, but none small enough to git it on howiver much dey pinched and squeezed. Poorer people came as well, but it was jus' de same wid dem. And in course, all de sarvants tried, but dey was out'n altogether. De young master was a-dying. Was dere nobody else, his mother exed, nobody at all, rich or poor? "No," dey telt her, everybody'd tried it excepting it was Mossycoat.

"Tell her to come at once," says de mistress.

So dey fetched her.

"Try dis slipper on," she says—dat's de mistress.

Mossycoat slips her foot into it easy enough; it fits her exac'ly. De young master jumps out o' bed, and is jus' a-going to tek her in his arms.

"Stop," she says, and runs off; but afore long she's back agen in her satin dress wid gowld sprigs, her gowld crown, and both her silver slippers. De young master is jus' a-going to tek her in his arms.

"Stop," she says, and agen she runs off. Dis time she comes back in her silk dress de color of all de birds o' de air. She don't stop him dis time, and as de saying used to be, he nearly eats her.

After when dey's all settled down agen, and is talking quiet-like, dere's one or two things as de master and mistress and de young master'ld like to know. How did she git to dance, and back agen, in no time, they exed her. "Jus' wishing," she says, and she tells 'em all as I've telt you about the magic coat her mother 'ed med for her, and de powers it give her if she cared to use 'em. "Yes, dat explains everything," dey says. Den dey bethinks theirselves of her saying as she came from where dey hit her on de head wid de skimmer. What did she mean by dat, dey wants to know. She meant jus' what she said, she telt 'em; it was always coming down on her head, pop, pop, pop. They were right angry when dey heard dat, and de whole of de kitchen sarvants was telt to go, and de dogs sent arter dem to drive de varmints right away from de place.

As soon as dey could Mossycoat and de young master got married, and she'd a coach and six to ride in, ai, ten if she liked, for you may be sure as she'd everything as she fancied. Dey lived happy ever after, and had a basketful o' children. I was dere when de owld son comed of age, a-playing de fiddle. But dat was many years back, and I shouldn't wonder if de owld master and mistress isn't dead by now, though I've niver heerd tell as dey was.

• 5 • *Little Rosy*

Recorded from Ruth L. Tongue, September 29, 1963, as she heard it from a Blackdown shepherd in Somerset in 1903. The tune was learned from Brendon Hills children, who sang it to a kind of singing game in Taunton in 1907.

This is Type 720, My Mother Slew Me; My Father Ate Me, The Juniper Tree. Key motifs are E613.0.1, "Reincarnation of murdered child as bird"; "G61, Relative's flesh eaten unwittingly"; N271, "Murder will out"; and "S31, Cruel stepmother." Type 720 is well-known in the Grimm version, No. 47, "The Juniper Tree," and is found throughout Europe. In England it is reported from Devonshire by Baring-Gould ("The Rose-tree" in Henderson, Northern Counties, pp. 314–17), from Yorkshire by Addy (Folk-Lore, VIII, 1897, "The Satin Frock," pp. 394–95), and from Lincolnshire by Gutch and Peacock (County Folk-Lore No. 5, "Orange and Lemon," p. 325). The School of Scottish Studies, Edinburgh, has two texts collected by Hamish Henderson, "Orangie and Applie" from Aberdeen, and a version of special interest from Perthshire, told by fourteen-year-old Jimmy McPhee. Here the murdered girl is brought back to her true form when her mother's grave is dug up and the ring turned on her finger. Published Scottish versions are in Robert Chambers, Popular Rhymes of Scotland, "The Milk-White Doo," p. 52, and Norah and William Montgomerie, The Well at the World's End (London, Hogarth Press, 1956), "Pippety

Pew," pp. 34–37. For the United States Baughman gives ten examples, eight from southern Negroes. Halpert discusses British variants in his note (p. 195) to an Ozark text (pp. 53–54), "Pennywinkle! Pennywinkle!" published by Vance Randolph in Who Blowed Up the Church House? *Stith Thompson speaks of its oral currency and cante-fable tendency in* The Folktale, *p. 116.*

The idea of the soul of the dead child growing out of the body as a tree, out of which a bird springs, is both widespread and primitive. The English singing game, "Old Roger is Dead," exemplifies a similar belief (Alice B. Gomme, The Traditional Games of England, Scotland, and Ireland, *II, 16–24).*

"Tallat" is an attic or loft; "marly" is marble.

THE JUNIPER TREE

My moth-er she killed me and put me in pies. My fa-ther he ate me and said I was nice. My broth-er and sis-ter they picked my bones, And they bur-ied me un-der they mar-ly stones, they mar-ly stones, they mar-ly stones. And they bur-ied me un-der they mar-ly stones.

• Rosy WERE A little maid as had a stepmother and her were so wicked and good-for-nothing as twopennorth of God-help-us stuck on a stick. Rosy hadn' no love for she.

One day she took 'n sended Rosy for to get some'at out of gurt chest up over in tallat. And the lid valled down on Rosy and killed 'n.

There her was with her head cutted off by thic lid, and thic wicked toad took'n and cooked'n and made she into pies vor her father and her two liddle sisters. And they took'n and they went and eat'n and like.'n too, and thic wicked toad her buried all they bones.

But Rosy her "comed again" like a ghostie bird all a-trembley and a-whivery and singeth:

> My Mammy her killed I 'n put I in pies
> My vather did eat I 'n 'er said I were nice
> My two liddle zisters they zucked my bones
> And buried I under they marly stones
> They marly stones, they marly stones
> And buried I under they marly stones.

And when her vather heard'n, he took a cold shiver, and he run, and the liddle zisters run too. And no one wouldn' neighbor with the wicked toad, zo her died lonesome.

• 6 • The Man Who Wouldn't Go Out at Night

Recorded from Ruth L. Tongue, September 29, 1963, as she heard it in Somerset at the Brompton Ralph Women's Institute in 1962. She knew other versions told between 1930 and 1940 by a blacksmith at Vellow, a cottage woman at Monksilver, and a farmer's wife at Elworthy.

Motifs present are M211, "Man sells soul to the devil," and K212, "Devil cheated by being frightened," both common in the humorous devil stories told throughout northern Europe. In

"Finn MacCuil and the Scotch Giant," in Patrick Kennedy,
Legendary Fictions of the Irish Celts *(London, 1866), pp. 203–
205, Finn's wife frightens away the giant with her witty tricks.
Captain Marryat retells the tale in his novel* Peter Simple.
  "Allerntide" is All Hallows. "To nursey" is to have a child.

• THERE WERE A varmer, a girt upstandable chap, and 'e wouldn't
go out arter dark not if it was ever so. 'Twas all very fine to
summertime, but when Allerntide come along and winter, 'twas
tur'ble bad for varm. There mid be stock to veed, an' cows to
milky, and lambs to help into this wordle, but 'e wouldn't go
out, no, not if you begged 'en. Well, 'is wife 'er were "goin' to
nursey," and 'er grew worrited. Supposing 'er should want
doctor night-time, 'e'd be bound to go vetch 'en, but no, 'e
wulldn't, not if 'twere ever so bad. Well then, 'er reckoned 'twas
summat bad, vor 'er knowed 'e were mortial vond o' she, zo 'er
gets around 'n until 'e tells 'er. When 'e were a silly young lad,
he'd sold 'isself, zee, and now time were nearly up, and Bogey
were a-waiting vor 'n. He couldn't catch 'en till dark, zo that
were why 'e bided indoors be'ind the lintel.

  Well, she began to think like, 'bout 'ow she could save the
man and the baby and the varm. So 'er gets a plough-coulter,
and 'er makes 'en red-'ot, and 'er puts 'en inside a girt pie-crust,
as 'ad a criss-cross o' salt on it. Then 'er do call out o' window,
"We be coming, zur, my man be a-coming, would 'ee like a bit
o' pie to goo on with?"

  Well, Bogey, 'e grab pie, and took a bite. Dunno what come
to 'is teeth with that little lot, but 'e was scorched bewtifull.
Then 'er up and 'er say, "Us won't be long, zur. We be a-coming,
zur." "Who be?" says Bogey, all of a sudden suspicious-like.
That there criss-cross o' salt 'ad fair burned 'e.

  "Why, I be a'coming, wi' my dear 'usband," says she, "to
cook vor 'ee both."

  Well, at that, they do tell, Bogey give a screech as zunk two
ships off Lundy, and took off away vor Tanton. And from what
I zee o' volks down there, I reckon 'e bided.

Part II
Legends

·7· Fairy Merchandise

Recorded by Katharine M. Briggs from Ruth L. Tongue, September 28, 1963. Miss Tongue heard the story as a child from haymakers at Galmington, near Taunton in Somerset, in the summer of 1906.

Motifs here are F342.1, "Fairy Gold"; F258.1, "Fairies hold a fair"; and Q41, "Politeness rewarded." Fairy people in England and Scandinavia commonly give a gift of seemingly useless things that turn to gold if kept. An account of a fairy fair near Taunton is also given in Keightley, The Fairy Mythology, pp. 294–95; and Hartland, English Fairy and Other Folk Tales, pp. 139–41, although here the human intruder is lamed. The necessity for politeness in dealing with supernatural people is stressed throughout Europe; e.g., see Type 480, The Spinning-Women by the Spring.

Legends with the present motifs are found in Sikes, British Goblins, pp. 120–24; and Hartland in The Science of Fairy Tales discusses them at length in his two chapters on "Fairy Births and Human Midwives." Their distribution runs from China to northern Europe.

• THERE WERE A varmer over-right our place did zee the vairies to their market and come whoame zafe tew. Mind, he didn't never vorget tew leave hearth clean 'n a pail of well water vor'n at night, 'n a girt dish o' scalt cream tew. My granny did say her'd get'n ready vor'n many's the time. Zo when her [the farmer] rode up tew stall, zee, all among the vair, 'n axed mannerly vor a zider mug ahanging up, the vairies answers 'n zo purty as if they was to Tanton Market. With that the varmer lugs out his money bags 'n pays, 'n what do 'ee believe! They gived 'n a heap of dead leaves vor his change, quite ser'ous like. Varmer he took 'n mannerly 'n ser'ous tew; then he wishes 'n "Good night, arl," 'n he ride whoame. He d' put zider mug on table 'n spread they dead leaves round un careful, then he d' zay,

"Come morn they won't none o' they be yur, but 'twere worth
it tew zee the liddle dears' market."

Come morn when Varmer went tew get his dew-bit avore
ploughing what dew her zee on table but a vine silver mug,
'n lumps of gold all around 'n.

·8· *Goblin Combe*

*Collected by Ruth L. Tongue who heard the account told in
chorus by two old ladies from Clevedon, Somerset, in 1945.*

*Central motifs are F211.2, "Fairyland entrance under a
stone," and J2415, "Foolish imitation of a lucky man." The latter
motif is prominent in Type 503, The Gifts of the Little People,
widely reported from northern Europe, with scattered examples
from the New World and from as far east as Japan. See Nos.
36, 37 in Folktales of Japan, a companion volume in this series.*

*Primroses and cowslips are both fairy flowers in English
country tradition.*

· THERE WAS A parcel of children and they was a-picking primroses, see, and one poor little dear her wandered away on her
lone self right down into Goblin Combe. She were only a little
trot, see, and didn't know no better. Well, when she do find she's
a-lost she cries, and the tears do run down her dear little face,
and dap on her pinafore like summer rain, and she do throw her
little self a-down in her grief and the primroses they knocks
against a rock. Then the rock opens and there's the fairises all
come to comfort her tears. They do give her a gold ball and
they lead the dear little soul safe home—on account she was
carrying primroses, see.

Well, 'twas the wonder of the village and the conjuror he gets
the notion he'd aget his fistes on more than one gold ball when
next the fairises opened the hill. So he do pick a bunch of primroses and he go on up Goblin Combe, and he was glad enough
to get in to the rock after all he see and hear on the way up.

Well, 'twasn't the right day, nor the right number of primroses, and he wasn't no dear little soul—*so they took him!*

·9· *The Fairy Follower*

Recorded from Ruth L. Tongue, September 29, 1963, who heard the story as a child told by a maid from the Welsh Marches.

A number of familiar motifs are present here. Those involving fairies include F234.2.5, "Fairy in form of beautiful young woman"; F236.1.6, "Fairy in green clothes"; and F363, "Fairies cause death." Also evident are D1272, "Magic circle," and F404, "Means of summoning spirits."

E. S. Hartland in "The Treasure on the Drim," Folk-Lore Journal, VI (1888), 125–28, gives two Welsh variants of evoking spirits through a magic circle, and the subsequent death of the person who called them up. In her study of Ritual Magic, E. M. Butler presents at length accounts from literary sources, such as Reginald Scot's Discoverie of Witchcraft (1584), of necromancers summoning demons, ghosts, and fairies. Similar to the present tale is an ill-fated experience befalling a blacksmith's son, which Butler quotes from The Spectre, or News of the Invisible World, London, 1836 (in the Noonday Press edition, New York, 1959, pp. 281–82). A similar spell for obtaining sight of the fairies is found in a seventeenth-century manuscript in the Bodleian Library, Oxford (e Mus 173).

• THERE WAS ONCE a lad, and he loved a girl with all his heart, and all he wanted was to marry her. His love was so hot that he could not bear to wait, but set to to get help from the fairies. It was an unchancy thing to do, and he set about it the wrong way. First he took a fair white cloth without asking the farmer's wife's leave, and no good could come of that. Then he filled a pail of river water, and that wouldn't do. Then he tried a pail of well water, and that wouldn't do. At last, he filled a pail of clear spring water, and that was right enough, but he stood it outside the door on the night of the new moon, instead of inside, so nothing came of that. So he had to wait a whole month, till the next new moon, and for two nights running, he set the pail inside the door, but that wasn't good enough, and still nothing happened. So he waited another month; it was May by this time, and he swept the hearth, and put the pail of water to stand on it, two nights before the new moon, and that was right. Just after midnight, he tiptoed down to the pail, and there was a thin gold oil on top of the water. He skimmed it off, and made a cake of it, with meal, and set it down on the fair white cloth. He made a circle and said the words and waited.

The door opened, and a dark fairy came in, and stretched out her hand for the cake.

"Not for thee," he said, and he shouldn't have spoken.

Then a fair fairy came in, and stretched out her hand. He tapped her on the wrist and said, "Not for thee." But he shouldn't have touched her.

Then came a most beautiful lady in green, and she said, "For me," and ate the cake.

After that she was always with him, and he told her his wishes. She granted them right enough, but in a back-handed way that turned them all to bitterness. He wanted marriage, and he got it, but with a cruel old woman, the richest in the parish. So he had his money too, and small good it did him. Then a great pestilence came on the place, and people died to the right and left of him, and his poor pretty sweetheart, whom he had loved all his life, was the first to die. But the lad's great strength bore him through everything, and it seemed he could not die. But at length the fairy at his elbow, meddling and urging him this way and that, though no one else could see her, wore him down to a thread and he died. As he lay in his coffin, a dark, cloudy shadow came down over it, and out of the darkness a voice said, very cold and clear, "For me."

· 10 · Pixy Fair

Collected by Ruth L. Tongue from a farmer's daughter on the Quantock Hills, South West, in Somerset in 1960.

The central motif is F352, "Theft of a cup (drinking horn) from the fairies." Legends of cup thefts are given in Thomas Keightley, The Fairy Mythology (*London, 1860*), *pp. 283–85, 292–93, the best known being "The Luck of Eden Hall." E. S. Hartland in* The Science of Fairy Tales (*London, 1891*), *pp. 48–50, chap. 6, "Robberies from Fairyland," gives many similar traditions, as well as examples of fairy gold (F342.1) turning to coal or leaves. Christiansen classifies the type as 6045, "Drinking Cup Stolen from the Fairies" in* The Migratory Legends, *and prints two texts in* Folktales of Norway, *a companion volume in this series, Nos. 52a, 52c, "The Drinking Horn Stolen from the Huldre-Folk." See also W. A. Craigie,* Scandinavian Folk-Lore (*London, 1896*), *p. 132, "One-Leg and the Stolen Goblet."*

In West Quantock dialect, well-illustrated in this tale, the word for lame, applied to a horse, is "scramble-footed"; to a man, "crippled"; and to a woman, "hobbled."

· 'AVE 'EE YEARD 'bout th' old man that come whoame from Markut? He wuz comin' up road loike when 'er zaw th' girt Pixy Vair, an' on one o' the starls there he zaw a gold mug vull up the top o' gold pieces. Zo 'er thart to 'isself, "Ef I d' grab 'ee I shall 'ave 'nuff money vur rest of me loife."

Zo with no more ado he d' gallop right on dru Pixy Vair, laying hold to mug as her went, and went on whoame as vast as pony's legs 'ood carry 'n. Highly delighted with proize he took 'n to bed vor zafe-keeping. Well, next marnin' vust thing he looks at was his mug—but 't 'ad gone. And what do 'ee think—arl there was was a girt twoad-stool. And when 'ee goes out t' get pony 'e finds 'tis scramble-footed, an' zo 'twas 'er was like it the rest of 'er days.

· 11 · *The Fairy Midwife*

Recorded from Ruth L. Tongue, September 28, 1963, who heard the tale as a child in Taunton and Trull, Somerset, and remembers this version from "Annie's Granny."

This is one of the oldest and most widely known of the fairy legends in England. The earliest form, close to the present text, is from Gervase of Tilbury in the thirteenth century. See E. S. Hartland, "Peeping Tom and Lady Godiva," Folk-Lore, I (1890), pp. 207–26, esp. 213.

Common motifs present here are F372.1, "Fairies take human midwife to attend fairy woman"; F235.4.1, "Fairies made visible through use of ointment"; and F378.6, "Tabu: using fairy bath water, soap, or ointment on oneself while bathing fairy child."

Legends embodying these motifs are found throughout Great Britain and northern Europe. See G. F. Black, County Folk-Lore, No. 3, edited by N. W. Thomas (London, 1903), pp. 26–28, from Shetland; Mrs. Bray, The Borders of the Tamar and the Tavy, *2 vols. (London, 1879), pp. 174–77, from Devonshire; Francis J. Child,* The English and Scottish Popular Ballads, *No. 39, "Tam Lin" and No. 40, "The Queen of Elfan's Nourice"; R. Th. Christiansen,* The Migratory Legends, *5070, "Midwife to the Fairies"; E. S. Hartland,* The Science of Fairy Tales, *pp. 59–67; Robert Hunt,* Popular Romances of the West of England, *First Series, pp. 110–16; Thomas Keightley,* The Fairy Mythology, *pp. 301–303, 310–12; Patrick Kennedy,* Legendary Fictions of the Irish Celts, *pp. 117–21; Wirt Sikes,* British Goblins, *pp. 86–88, from Wales.*

· THERE WAS AN old body who was asked by the vairies to come and look after their babies. She was well fed and clothed and had never been so happy—but of course she would go and rub her eyes with their fairy ointment—just to make sure " 'Twouldn' hurt the pretty dears" and then she saw too much!

Next year she had a stall at Taunton Market and she saw the

vairies picking and stealing shamefully. "Thee shan't steal none of my vairings," she said out loud. They came all around her like a cloud of angry wasps and when they'd gone her eyesight was gone too!

·12· *The Green Mist*

Reprinted from M. C. Balfour, "Legends of the Lincolnshire Cars," Folk-Lore, II (1891), pp. 259–64, as told by an old man from Lindsey. Mrs. Balfour comments on the Lincolnshire people: "I may say, in spite of their receptiveness towards things marvellous, that they were otherwise practical and somewhat unimaginative, and accepted the tales they had heard from their fathers with respect, indeed, but were content not to ask themselves for absolute belief."

This is Type 1187, Meleager, with an unusual variation from the original form in which the hero lives as long as the brand burning on the hearth lasts; here, the heroine may live until the cowslip withers. Important motifs are E765, "Life bound up with external object or event," and E765.3.4, "Girl lives until her cowslip is pulled." The tale is sparsely distributed in northern Europe. Baughman cites English variants from Wales and Perthshire, and American ones from New York and New Jersey.

"Mools" is soil; "spud," turf; "yarth," earth; "thruff," through; "cromm'le," crumble; "fither," whether; "quare," queer.

· So THOU'ST heerd tell o' th' boggarts an' all the horrid things o' th' au'd toimes? Ay, they wor mischancy, onpleasant sort o' bodies to do wi', an' a'm main glad as they wor all go'an afore ma da'ays. I ha' niver seed nowt o' that sort, 'cep mappen a bogle or so—nuthin' wu'th tellin' of. But if thou likes them sort o' tales, a' can tell thee some as ma au'd gran'ther tould us when a' wor nobbut a tiddy brat. He wor main au'd, nigh a hunner year, fo'ak said; an' a wor ma fa'ather's gran'ther reetly speakin',

so tha can b'leeve as a knowed a lot 'bout th' au'd toimes. Mind,
a wunnot say as ahl th' ta'ales be treu'ue; but ma gran'ther said
as they wor, an' a b'leeved un ahl hissel'. Annyways, a'll tell um
as a heerd um, and that's ahl as a can do.

Wa'al, i' they times fo'ak mun ha' bin geyan unloike to now.
'Stead o' doin' their work o' da'ays, 'n smokin' ther pipes o'
Sundays, i' peace 'n comfort, tha wor allus botherin' ther heads
'bout summat 'r other—or the cho'ch wor doin' it for 'um. Th'
priests wor allus at 'un 'bout thur sowls; an' what wi' hell an'
th' boggarts, ther moinds wor niver aisy. An' ther wor things
as didn't 'long to th' cho'ch, an' yit—a can't reetly 'splain to
'ee; but th' fo'ak had idees o' ther oa'n, an' wa'ays o' ther oa'n,
as a'd kep' oop years an' years, an' *hunnerds* o' years, since th'
toime when ther worn't no cho'ch, leastwise no cho'ch o' that
sort; but tha gi'n things to th' bogles 'n sich, to kep' 'un friendly.
Ma gran'ther said 's how the bogles 'd wanst bin thowt a deal
more on, an' at da'arklins ivery night th' fo'ak'd bear loights i'
ther han's roon ther ha'ouses, sa'ain' wo'ds to kep' 'um off; an'
a'd smear blo'ood o' th' doorsil' to skeer away th' horrors; an' a'd
put bread an' salt o' th' flat stouns set oop by th' la'ane side to
get a good ha'arvest; an' a'd spill watter i' th' fower co'orners
o' th' fields, when a wanted ra'in; an' they thowt a deal on th'
sun, fur tha reckoned as a ma'ade th' yarth, an' browt th' good
an' ill chances, an' a do'ant know what ahl. A can't tell 'ee reetly
what they b'leeved; fur 'twor afore ma gran'ther's toime, ahl
that, an' that's more'n a hunnerd an' fifty years agone, seest tha;
but a reckon tha made nigh iverythin' as they seed an' heerd
into sort o' gre'at bogles, an' tha wor allus gi'un 'um things, or
sa'ayin' so't o' prayers loike, to keep 'um fro' doin' th' fo'ak anny
evil.

Wa'al, that wor a long toime agone, as a said afore, an' 'twas
no'an so bad i' ma gran'ther's day; but natheless, 'twor't forgot,
an' some o' th' fo'ak b'leeved it ahl still, an' said au'd prayers
or spells loike, o' th' sly. So ther wor, so to sa'ay, two
cho'ches, th' wan wi' priests an' can'les, an' a' that; th' other
just a lot o' au'd ways, kep' oop ahl onbeknown an' hidden loike
mid th' fo'ak thersels; an' they thowt a deal more, ma gran'ther
said, on th' au'd spells, 's on th' sarvice i' th' cho'ch itsel'. But's

toime went on, tha two got so't o' mixed oop; an' some o' th' fo'aks cudn't ha tould thee ef 'twor fur one or t'other as tha done th' things.

To Yule, i' th' cho'ches thur wur gran' sarvices, wi' can'les an' flags an' what not; an' i' th' cottages ther wor can'les an' ca'akes an' gran' doin's; but the priests niver knowed as many o' th' fo'ak wor on'y wakin' th' dyin' year, an' 'at tha wine teemed upo' th' doorsil to first cock-crow, wor to bring good luck i' th' new year. An' a reckon' some o' th' fo'ak thersel'd do th' au'd heathen wa'ays an' sing hymns meantime, wi' neer a thowt o' tha strangeness o't.

Still, ther wor many's kep' to th' au'd wa'ays ahl together, thoff tha did it hidden loike, an' a'am goin' to tell 'ee of wan fambly as ma gran'ther knowed fine, an' how they waked th' spring wan year.

As a said afore, a can't, even ef a wud, tell 'ee ahl th' things as tha useter do; but theer was wan toime o' th' year 's they partic'larly went in fur ther spells an' prayers, an' that wor early spring. Tha thowt as th' yarth wor sleepin' ahl th' winter, an' 'at th' bogles—ca'all um what 'ee wull—'d nobbut to do but mis-chief, for they'd nowt to see to i' th' fields. So they wor feared on th' long da'ark winter da'ays 'n noights, i' th' mid o' ahl so'ts o' unseen fearsome things, ready 'n waitin' fur a chance to play un evil tricks.

But as the winter went by, they thowt as 'twor toime to wake th' yarth fro' its sleepin' 'n set th' bogles to wo'k, carin' fur th' growin' things 'n bringing th' harvest. Efter that th' yarth wor toired, an' wor sinkin' to sleep agen an' tha useter sing hushieby songs i' th' fields o' th' autumn evens. But i' th' spring, tha want—th' fo'ak did as b'leeved i' th' au'd wa'ays—to every field in to'n, 'n lifted a spud o' yarth fro' the mools; an' tha said stra'ange an' quare wo'ds, as tha cudn't sca'arce unnerstand thersels; but th' same as 'd bin said for hunnerds o' years. An' ivery mornin' at th' first dawn, tha stood o' th' door-sil, wi' salt an' bread, i' ther han's, watchin' an' waitin' for th' Green Mist 's rose fro' th' fields 'n tould 'at th' yarth wor awake again; an' th' life wor comin' to th' trees an' th' pla'ants, an' th' seeds wor bustin' wi' th' beginning o' th' spring.

Wa'al, ther wor wan fambly as'd done ahl that, year arter
year, for's long as they knowed of; jest 's ther gran'fathers'd done
it afore un. An' wan winter e'en nigh on a hunnerd an' thurty
year gone t' now, tha wor makin' ready for wakin' the spring.
Th' 'ad had a lot o' trooble thruff th' winter, sickness an' what
not 'd bin bad i' th' pla'ace; an' th' darter, a rampin' young
maid, wor growed whoite 'n wafflin' loike a bag o' boans, 'stead
o' bein' th' purtiest lass i' th' village, as a'd bin afore. Da'ay arter
da'ay a growed whoiter an' sillier, till a cudn't stan' upo's feet
more'n a new born babby, an' a cud on'y lay at th' winder,
watchin' an' watchin' th' winter crep' awa'ay.

An' "Oh, Mother," a'd kep' a-sa-ayin' ower an' ower agin,
"ef a cud on'y wake th' spring with 'ee agean, mebbe th' Green
Mist 'd mek me strong n' well, loike th' trees an' th' flowers, an'
the co'n i' th' fields."

An' tha mother'd comfort her loike, an' promise 'a she'd coom
wi' 'em agin to th' wakin', and grow strong an' straight 's iver.
But da'ay arter da'ay a got whiter an' wanner, till a looked, ma
gran'ther said, loike a snow-fla'ake fadin' i' th' sun. An' da'ay
arter da'ay th' winter crep' by, an' th' wakin' o' th' spring wor
a'most theer. Th' pore maid watched an' waited for th' toime fur
goin' to th' fields; but a'd got so weak an' sick 'at a knowed a
cudn't git ther wi' th' rest. But a wudn't gi'n oop for ahl that,
an's mother mun sweer 'at she'd lift th' lass to th' door-sil, at th'
comin' o' th' Green Mist, so's a mowt toss out th' bread an' salt
o' th' yarth her o'an sel' an' wi' her o'an pore thin han's. An'
still th' da'ays went by, an' th' fo'ak wor goin' o' yarly morns,
to lift th' spud i' th' fields; an' th' coming o' th' Green Mist wor
lookit for ivery dawning.

An' wan even th' lass, as'd bin layin' wi's eyes fixed o' th' little
gyarden, said to 's mother:

"Ef the Green Mist don't come i' th' morn's dawnin', a'll not
can wait fur 't longer. Th' mools is ca'allin' ma, an' th' seeds
is burstin' as'll bloom ower ma head; a know't wa'al, Mother—
'n yit, ef a cud on'y see th' spring wake wanst agin! Mother, a
sweer a'd axe no more'n to live 's long 's wan o' them cowslips
as coom ivery year by th' ga'ate, an' to die wi' th' furst on 'em
when th' summer's in."

The mother whisht tha maid in fear, fur tha bogles an' things as they b'leeved in wor allus gainhand, an' cud hear owt as wor said. They wor niver safe, niver aloan, the pore foak to than, wi th' things as tha cudn't see, an' th' things as tha cudn't hear, allus roon 'em. But th' dawn o' th' next da'ay browt th' Green Mist.

A com'd fro' th' mools, an' wrapped asel' roon iverythin', green's th' grass i' summer sunshine, 'n sweet-smellin' as th' yarbs o' th' spring, an' th' lass wor carried to th' door-sill, wheer a croom'led th' bread 'n salt, on to th' yarth wi's oan han's, an' said th' stra'ange au'd wo'ds o' welcoming to th' new spring. An' a lookit to th' ga'ate wheer th' cowslips growed, an' thon wor took ba'ack to's bed by th' winder, when a slep' loike a babby, an' dreamt o' summer an' flowers an' happiness.

Fur, fither 'twor th' Green Mist as done it, a can't tell ee more'n ma gran'ther said, but fro' that day, a growed stronger n' prettier nor iver, an' by th' toime th' cowslips wor buddin', a wor runnin' about an' laughin' loike a very sunbeam i' th' au'd cottage. But ma gran'ther tould as a wor allus so white 'n wan, while a lookit loike a will-o'-th'-wyke flittin' aboot; an' o' th' could da'ays a'd sit shakin' ower th' foire, an' a'd look nigh de'ad, but when th' sun'd coom oot, a'd da'ance an' sing i' th' loight, an' stretch oot's arms to't 's if a on'y lived i' th' warmness o't. An' by 'n by th' cowslips burst ther buds, an' coom i' flower, an' th' maid wor growed so stra'ange an' beautiful 'at they wor nigh feared on her. An' ivery mornin' a'd kneel by th' cowslips, 'n watter 'n tend 'em, 'n da'ance to 'em, i' th' sunshine, while th' mother'd stand beggin' her to leave 'em, an' cried 'at she'd have 'em pu'd oop by th' roots 'n throwed awa'ay. But th' lass on'y looked stra'ange at a, 'n say, soft an' low loike, "Ef thee aren't tired o' ma, Mother, niver pick wan o' them flowers. They'll fade o' thersels soon enuff—ay, soon enuff—thou knows."

An' tha mother'd go'a back to th' cottage, 'n greet ower th' wo'k; but a niver said nowt of her trouble to th' neebors, not till arter'ds. But wan da'ay a lad o' th' village stopped at th' ga'ate to chat wi' 'em, an' by an' by, whiles a wor gossipin' a picked a cowslip 'n pla'ayed wi' it. Th' lass didn' see what a'd done; but as he said goodbye, a seed th' flower as'd fa'allen to th'

yarth at's feet. "Did thee pull that cowslip?" a said, lookin'
stra'ange an' white, wi' wan han' laid ower her heart.

"Ay," says he, 'n lifting it oop a gin it to her, smilin' loike,
'n thinkin' what'n a pretty maid it wor.

She looked at th' flower, 'n at th' lad, an' ahl roon aboot her—
at th' green trees, an' th' sproutin' grass, an' th' yaller blooms,
an' oop at th' gowlden shinin' sun itself'—an' ahl to wanst,
shrinkin' 'sif th' loight a'd loved so mooch wor brennin' her, a
ran into th' hoose, wi'oot a spoken word on'y a so't o' cry, loike
a dumb beast i' pain, an' th' cowslip catched close agin her heart.

An' then—b'leeve it or not as 'ee wull—a niver spoak agin,
but la'ay on th' bed, starin' at th' flower in's han' an' fadin' as it
faded all thruff the da'ay. An' at th' dawnin' ther wor on'y layin'
on th' bed a wrinkled, whoite shrunken dead thing, wi' in's han'
a shrivelled cowslip; an' th' mother covered 't ower wi' th'
clo'es, an' thowt o' th' beautiful joyful maid da'ancin' loike a
bird i' th' sunshine by th' gowden noddin' blossoms, on'y the
da'ay goan by. Th' bogles 'd heerd a, an' a'd gi'n's wish. A'd
bloomed wi' th' cowslips, an' a'd fa'aded wi' th' first on 'em!
An' ma gran'ther said as 'twor ahl 's treue's death!

·*13*· *The Apple-Tree Man*

*Recorded from Ruth L. Tongue, September 28, 1963, as she
heard it from an old man at Pitminster, Somerset, about 1920.
Miss Tongue comments: "Pitminster was the place where in my
childhood I was gravely and proudly conducted by a farm-child
to a very old apple tree in their orchard and told mysteriously
that it was 'the Apple-Tree Man.' In 1958 I heard of him again
on the Devon-Somerset borders."*

*Common motifs here are B251.1.2, "Animals speak to one
another at Christmas"; N541.1, "Treasure reveals itself only on
Christmas at midnight (or Christmas Eve)"; N511.1.9,
"Treasure buried under tree"; and N471, "Foolish attempt of
second man to overhear secrets."*

American legends containing Motif B251.1.2 are known from

North Carolina (Brown Collection, *I, 637*), *and Mississippi* (*Dorson*, Negro Folktales in Michigan, *pp. 152–53*).

   "Borough English" was a local inheritance custom in various country districts, by which the farm came to the youngest son instead of to the eldest, who was supposed to have already made his way in the world. This ancient form of land tenure long survived in Pitminster. It has sometimes been suggested that it was this custom which made it seem right to folk storytellers that the youngest son of the king should inherit the throne before his brothers. It is clear, however, from this story that the system aroused some criticism.

   A "dunk" is a donkey; a "natomy," a skeleton; "quarter-ail," paralysis; and "diddicky," rotten.

• THERE WERE A hard-working chap as was eldest of a long family, see, zo when his Dad die there wasn't nothing left for he. Youngest gets it all, and he do give bits and pieces to all his kith; but he don't like eldest, see, spoilt young hosebird he were, so all he do let he have is his Dad's old dunk, and a ox that was gone to a natomy (I s'pose it had the quarter-ail), and a tumbledown cottage with the two-dree ancient old apple-trees where his Dad had lived to with his granfer. The chap don't grumble, but he go cutting grass along lane, and old dunk begun to fatten, and he do rub the ox with herbs and say the words, and old ox he perk up hisself and walk smart, and then he do turn they beastses into orchet, and they old apple-trees flourish a marvel.

   But it don't leave him no time to find the rent! Oh yes, youngest was bound to have his rent. Dap on the dot too!

   Then one day he come into orchet and say, " 'Twill be Christmas Eve come tomorrow, when beasts do talk. There's a treasure hereabouts we've all heard tell, and I'm set to ask your dunk. He mustn't refuse to tell me. Yew wake me just afore midnight and I'll take a whole sixpence off the rent."

   Come Christmas Eve the chap 'e give old dunk and ox a bit extra and he do fix a bit of holly in the shippen, and he gets his last mug of cider, and mull it by ashen faggot, and outs to the orchet to give'n to the apple trees. . . . Then the Apple-Tree Man he calls to the chap and 'e say, "Yew take and look under this gurt diddicky root of ours." And there was a chest full of finest gold. " 'Tis yours, and no one else," say the Apple-Tree Man. "Put'n away zafe and bide quiet about'n." So he done that. "Now yew can go call your dear brother," say Apple-Tree Man, " 'tis midnight."

Well, youngest brother he do run out in a terrible hurry-push and sure enough the dunk's a-talking to the ox. "Yew do know thic gurt greedy fule that's a-listening to we, so unmannerly, he do want we should tell where treasure is."

"And that's where he never won't get it," say the ox. "Cause someone have a-tooked he already."

·14· *Tibb's Cat and the Apple-Tree Man*

Recorded from Ruth L. Tongue, September 28, 1963, as she heard it about 1910 from "Annie's Granny." The title of the tale was noted on the back of a school exercise book.

This story also deals with the Apple-Tree Man of the preceding tale, and contains Motif D950.10, "Magic apple tree." There is a suggestion of Motif G243, "Witch's sabbath."

A "dairy maid" is a white and tortoise-shell cat. There is a saying round Pitminster, "You want to know too much, like Tibb's cat."

· THERE WAS A little cat down Tibb's Farm, not much more'n a kitten—a little dairy-maid with a face so clean as a daisy. A pretty little dear her was, but her wanted to know too much. There was fields down along as wasn't liked. No one cared much about working there. Y'see, 'twas all elder there, and there was a queer wind used to blow there most times, and sound like someone talking it would. I wouldn't go there myself unless I had a criss-cross of salt on a crust. Oh! yes, my maid, I could show 'ee the field now, but I 'on't, and don't you be like Tibb's cat, and go look-see for yourself! There's summat bad about down there, and that was why all they wild black cats goed there on certain nights, and Tibb's cat she wished to go too. She tried to find the way Candlemas Eve, and Allern [Hallowe'en] and all the wisht nights witches do meet, but her weren't big enough to catch up. So, when New Year's Eve come, she tried again.

This time she got as far as the orchet, and then the Apple-Tree Man he called out to her, "Yew go on back whoame, my dear. There's folk a-coming to pour cider for my roots, and shoot off guns to drive away the witches. This be no place for yew. Yew go back whoame, and don't come awandering round at night till St. Tibb's Eve."

The little dairy-maid her took off home with her tail stiff with vright. Properly scared she, the Apple-Tree Man did. And she never wandered at night again, 'cause she didn't know when St. Tibb's Eve is. Nor do anybody else.

•15• The Man in the Wilderness

Recorded from Ruth L. Tongue, September 28, 1963, who heard it from her grandmother, Elizabeth Carr, who was told it by her *mother about 1860. Mrs. Carr came from a farm in Lincolnshire.*

The most relevant motif here is G681, "Ogre gives riddle on pain of death," known in Germany, the Slavic countries, and India.

The tale was repeated always in the same words so that the children learned it by heart. As a rhyming riddle "The Man in the Wilderness" is a well-known nursery rhyme. See James Orchard Halliwell-Phillipps, The Nursery Rhymes of England *(London, 1843, No. CCCLXIX, pp. 157, 209), who refers to a seventeenth-century MS text in the Sloane Collection. Beatrix Potter in her story for children,* The Tale of Squirrel Nutkin *(London, 1903), p. 33, makes use of it, along with other traditional riddles. Riddling tests are common in folklore; "The Fause Knight upon the Road" (Child No. 3) is a familiar example. The Red Sea was the usual place to which malignant spirits were banished.*

It is possible that the story may have been inspired by the
6

rhyme and invented by the great-grandmother, but even so it
has existed in oral tradition for four generations.

• Tom, Dick and Jack were going to the Fair. They came to a
wood where there was a Bad 'un, and no one could send him to
the Red Sea. He asked travelers a question, and if they couldn't
tell it they were never seen any more. So Tom says, "I'm the
eldest, I'll go in first."

So they waited. By and by Tom came back, and he said,

> The Man in the Wilderness asked of me
> "How many blackberries grow in the sea?"
> I answered him as I thought good,
> "As many red herrings as grow in the wood."

"And he had to let me go."

So Dick said, "Now it's my turn."

And they waited, and by and by, Dick came back, and he
said,

> The Man in the Wilderness asked me why
> His hen could swim, and his pig could fly.
> I answered him briskly as I thought best,
> "Because they were born in a cuckoo's nest."

"And he had to let me go."

Then it was little Jacky's turn. So they waited, and all of a
sudden there was a great puff of smoke, and by and by little
Jacky came back and said,

> The Man in the Wilderness asked me to tell
> The sands in the sea and I counted them well.
> Says he with a grin, "And not one more?"
> I answered him bravely, "You go and make sure!"

"So he had to go, and the Bad 'uns in the Red Sea will keep
him."

Then Tom, Dick, and little Jacky went to the Fair quite safely.

·16· *The Old Man at the White House*

Reprinted from S. O. Addy, "Four Yorkshire Folktales," Folk-Lore, VIII (1897), pp. 393–94, told by Richard Hirst, age 18, of Sheffield.

Central motifs are C420.2. "Tabu: not to speak about a certain happening," and D1825.4.3, "Magic power to see lost things." G. L. Kittredge in Witchcraft in Old and New England *(Cambridge, Mass., 1929), p. 165, discusses the power of witches to recover lost articles. The ending of Type 366,* The Man from the Gallows, *has a ghost seizing a man who robbed his corpse. Mark Twain's "The Man with the Golden Arm" similarly scares the listener. The traditional version of this was published in Jacob's* English Fairy Tales, *p. 138.*

· THERE WAS ONCE a man who lived in a white house in a certain village, and he knew everything about everybody who lived in the place.

In the same village there lived a woman who had a daughter called Sally, and one day she gave Sally a pair of yellow gloves and threatened to kill her if she lost them.

Now Sally was very proud of her gloves, but she was careless enough to lose one of them. After she had lost it she went to a row of houses in the village and inquired at every door if they had seen her glove. But everybody said "No," and she was told to go and ask the old man that lived in the white house.

So Sally went to the white house and asked the old man if he had seen her glove. The old man said, "I have thy glove, and I will give it thee if thou wilt promise me to tell nobody where thou hast found it. And remember, if thou tells anybody I shall fetch thee out of bed when the clock strikes twelve at night."

So he gave the glove back to Sally.

But Sally's mother got to know about her losing the glove, and said, "Where did you find it?"

Sally said, "I daren't tell, for if I do the old man will fetch me out of bed at twelve o'clock at night."

Her mother said, "I will bar all the doors and fasten all the windows and then he can't get in and fetch thee." And she made Sally tell her where she had found her glove.

So Sally's mother barred all the doors and fastened all the windows, and Sally went to bed at ten o'clock that night and began to cry. At eleven she began to cry louder, and at twelve o'clock she heard a voice saying in a whisper, but gradually getting louder and louder:

"Sally, I'm up one step."
"Sally, I'm up two steps."
"Sally, I'm up three steps.'
"Sally, I'm up four steps."
"Sally, I'm up five steps."
"Sally, I'm up six steps."
"Sally, I'm up seven steps."
"Sally, I'm up eight steps."
"Sally, I'm up nine steps."
"Sally, I'm up ten steps."
"Sally, I'm up eleven steps."
"Sally, I'm up twelve steps!"
"Sally, I'm at thy bedroom door!!"
"SALLY, I HAVE HOLD OF THEE!!!"

· 17 ·   *Why the Donkey is Safe*

Recorded from Ruth L. Tongue, September 29, 1963, who heard it from an old gipsy woman in Worthywood above Porlock Weir, Somerset, in 1941.

The sign of the cross on a donkey's back is supposed to protect it from witchcraft. T. F. Thiselton Dyer refers to the "common superstition" that the cross on the donkey comes from Christ's having ridden it (English Folk-Lore, London, 1878, p. 119). Also pertinent is G303.16.3, "Devils driven away by cross." A

Sunday-born child is "free from the malice of evil spirits and
safe from the effects of over-looking and ill-wishing" (E. and
M. A. Radford, Encyclopedia of Superstitions (New York,
1949), pp. 231–32. In Somerset, according to Ruth Tongue, a
witch who inadvertently curses a Sunday-born child finds the
curse rebounding on herself. In No. 19 (this volume), "The Sea
Morgan and the Conger Eels," the boy sent to drive away the
mermaid was born on a Sunday. Also present is Motif
D1273.1.3, "Seven as a magic number."

"Galley-trap" is a Somerset name for a fairy ring, about which
it is believed that if a thief or murderer sets foot in the ring he
will end on the gallows.

• THERE WERE A little, small, young dunk foal, and 'e wanted to
take a look-see at life, so when 'is Mother weren't a-looking, 'e
trotted off on 'is wankly little legs. First go off, 'e met an old
witch.

"I'll 'ave 'ee," says she. But when 'er grab 'en, 'er got burnded.
"Yow," says she, "yew was born on a Sunday, I'll be bound!"

"Like all dunks, my Mammy do say," said the little, small,
young dunk foal, an' 'e went on an' on.

Next go off, 'e met Bogey.

"I'll 'ave 'ee," say Bogey. But when 'e grab 'en, 'is fistseses
fried. "Yow!" says Bogey, "yew got a criss-cross on your back.
I can't touch 'ee."

"Like all dunks," said the little, small, young dunk foal, an' 'e
went on along.

Then 'e come to a galley-trap, and pixies they come all about
'im.

"You go on out of that," say they. " 'Ere you come, just seven
days old, and a criss-cross on your back, and us can't ride 'ee."

"Like all dunks, my Mammy do say," said the little, small,
young dunk foal, and back 'e goed.

When 'e got 'ome, first 'is Mammy kick 'un for going astray,
and then 'er give 'en 'is dinner.

·18· The Hunted Soul

Recorded from Ruth L. Tongue, September 28, 1963, who heard it several times in Somerset: in 1922 from a visiting game-keeper in Crowcombe Valley; in 1935 from a farmer's wife in Coleford Water; and in 1940 from a Vellow blacksmith, who said, "Old Nick couldn't touch she on account the old cob was shod."

An almost identical story, also laid in Ellworthy, is given by Mrs. Bray in The Borders of the Tamar and the Tavy, *II, pp. 114–16. In Charlotte S. Burne and Georgina Jackson,* Shropshire Folk-Lore *(London, 1883), pp. 28–32, an onlooker who watches Wild Eric's Ride and speaks to the Wild Hunt suffers madness. Jacob Grimm devoted special attention to the Wild Hunt and its relation to witches in his* Teutonic Mythology, *III (tr. James Stallybrass, London, 1883), p. 1057. The Wild Hunt is well known in Germany and northern Europe.*

A number of applicable submotifs can be found under Motif E501, "The Wild Hunt," which has an extensive bibliography. Other motifs are G211.2.7, "Witch in form of a hare," and G273.4, "Witch powerless to cross stream."

Local names attached to the Wild Hunt are the "Devil and his Dandy Dogs," the "Yeth Hounds," and the "Gabriel Ratchets." John Masefield wrote a poem on "The Hounds of Hell," in which St Withiel volunteers to be pursued by the Wild Hunt (The Collected Poems of John Masefield, *London, 1923, pp. 639–55).*

· THERE WERE A old Goody as lived down to Coleford Water, and she used to come into Crowcombe market wi' 'er bits and 'er pieces, but she were a very stout old body, and 'er pony old Smart 'e were getting on in years now—reckon 'e were nearly forty—and so they used to get ready quite early in the morning, round about four o'clock, and start on. Well, one time, old

Goody she mistook the time; she got up, she got 'er things ready, put in the stockings, and the apples, and the eggses into the pannier, and she loaded 'er old Smart, and then she gets up 'erself on upping stock, and on to 'is back, and away they goes afore midnight.

Well, bye and bye, old Goody she began to feel a bit sleepy-like. Old Smart 'e were a-plodding on as 'e'd done all these years, and 'er began to nod, and must 'ave slept a bit, 'cos, when she woke up—summat waked she, and there were old Smart, a-standing in the middle o' sixty-acre, and 'e were a-trembling with fear. Ah! Sweat were be'ind 'is ears, and 'is mane and 'is tail they were stiff with fright; and Granny, she look around like and there she saw a little white rabbit hopping towards she, all terrified, and there come the sound of 'ounds be'ind. But they wasn't real 'ounds, oh! no, they dogs as do come across there, they ain't no real 'ounds; best not say too much about they. Well, when Granny see this little white rabbit, she were that sorry for 'er, she forgot white rabbits was witch-souls, and 'er took off lid o' the pannier, and white rabbit 'en 'opped in, and Granny clapped down the lid tight. Then she tried to get old Smart to move on, but 'e wasn't doing no moving, not 'e; 'e kept 'is eyes on a bit o' grass did old Smart—'e knowed a bit—'e wasn't going to look up. When Granny see that, she remembered, and she got out her knitting-needles, see, and went on with 'er stocking, and 'er 'eard they there dogs coming nearer and a clatter o' hoofs, and a girt fine black rider 'e come up alongside she. 'Is 'orse 'ad 'orns, and there was a green light round 'en, and they ther dogs 'ad green fire coming out o' their mouths.

" 'Ave 'e seen a rabbit go by?" say the rider.

Well! Granny knew better than to answer 'en, so she just shook 'er 'ead; and that weren't wrong neither, 'cos rabbit were in pannier! And away the whole hunt went up towards Will's Neck. You could 'ear their 'owls on the wind. And then old Smart, 'e get up, and 'e lumber up at a canter—a thing 'e 'adn't done for about twenty year, and 'e never stopped till 'e come to Roebuck Ford, and then 'e do stop. I said 'e knowed a thing or two, 'cos nothing can't 'arm 'ee if you be in the middle of running water. No witches nor devils nor nothing. Then Granny she lift up the lid o' 'er pannier, and out come the most beautiful lady.

"Oh!" says she, "how can I thank 'ee? When I were young, I were a witch, and when I died, I were condemned to be hunted forever by the Devil and 'is pack of Yeth-hounds, until I could get be'ind 'em. And now you've saved my soul."

And then she gave a most beautiful smile, all lit up like sunlight, and then she were gone. Well, Granny and old Smart, they made their way up along to Crowcombe. When they got to Buttercross, church clock were striking three! So they set theirselves down by the Cross, and they finished their sleep. It 'ad been a 'ard night for old folks, but they dogs couldn't 'arm they, on account the 'orse was shod, see?

19 · *The Sea Morgan and the Conger Eels*

Recorded from Ruth L. Tongue, September 29, 1963, who first heard the Somerset tradition mentioned in 1960 by an old man in Taunton Red Cross Disabled Club, and after hearing snatches of it, later secured the full account from a Stolford woman in Eddington Women's Institute.

Motifs here are F420.1.2.1, "Water-maidens are of unusual beauty"; F420.5.2.1, "Water-spirits lure mortal into water"; and D1273.1.5, "Twelve as a magic number." The Sunday child unharmed by spirits appears also in No. 17 (this volume), "Why the Donkey is Safe." Here he is also deaf; we recall that Ulysses temporarily deafened his sailors so that they could pass the sirens' rock without succumbing to their song. Rudyard Kipling in his story "Dymchurch Flit" (Puck of Pook's Hill) employs the folk theme of disability as an aid to a mortal dealing with supernatural beings.

Sea morgan is the name for a mermaid round the Severn Sea. The dangerous and alluring qualities of mermaids, known from classical times, are exemplified in the ballad of "Clerk Colvil" (Child No. 42), and Robert Chambers, "Lorntie and the Mer-

maid" (The Popular Rhymes of Scotland, *Edinburgh, 1826*),
pp. 279–80.
    A "steart-horse" is a mud-sledge.

• THERE WAS A sea morgan with a beautiful vace, and she'd sing
on autumn evenings and anyone who heard her had to go, and
they'd wade out further and further to reach her till the quicksands got them, and the conger eels got a feast. They always
knew when the eels barked she would be about that low tide, so
something was done to end her wicked ways.

There was a gifted woman had a deaf son, and he was born
on a Sunday, so she sent him to drive away the morgan. He
couldn't hear her voice, and as her hair was green, he didn't
think much of her. He got out his Steart Horse, and went out
over the flats with his eel-spear, and all the while she was singing, he was getting a fine haul of congers, and the sled kept him
from sinking in the quicksands. When he'd speared twelve of
them, she gave a skreek, and took herself off—and she never
come back. All Stolford and Steart had Conger-pie that week.

• 20 •   *Tarr Ball and the Farmer*

*Recorded from Ruth L. Tongue, September 28, 1963, as
she heard the tale in Somerset in 1942, from John Ash, a carter,
aged 70.*
    *The belief that "Fairies lead travelers astray" (Motif F369.7)
is common in England, Ireland, Wales, Canada, and the United
States. Other motifs present are F361.14, "Fairy punishes servant girl who fails to leave food for him," and F234.1.1, "Fairy
in form of cow (bull)."*
    *Shakespeare's Puck is thoroughly in this folk tradition. See
K. M. Briggs, The Anatomy of Puck (London, 1959), chap. 4,
"Shakespeare's Fairies." For examples in Great Britain see S. O.
Addy, Household Tales with Other Traditional Remains, p.
134; Mrs. Bray, The Borders of the Tamar and the Tavy, Letter
X; Thomas Keightley, The Fairy Mythology, p. 300; James*

MacDougall and George Calder, Folk Tales and Fairy Lore in Gaelic and English (*Edinburgh, 1910), pp. 281–83, 291–93. An Ozark variant is in Vance Randolph*, Who Blowed Up the Church House?' *pp. 123–24.*

"Barton" is byre or cowshed. "Unket" is uncanny.

• THERE WAS AN old curmudgeon of a fellow who lived down to Allerford, and he bought a farm at Lucott. He hadn't been there a night when he stopped servants setting out clean water and a dish of cream for the pixies. And the next day they just couldn't catch up with all there was to do in the house and stables. When next night came he went out to drive in four fine young heifers from Top Lawns, and off they galloped down rocky lane past Lucott hill, over Nutscale Ford and up onto Tarr Ball. Nobody heard the old man shout. He couldn't make a soul hear, not a soul! He couldn't make anyone hear at the Mill, nor the Shepherd's cottage, nor Little Combe, though he yelled hisself hoarse. So all down and over Nutscale Ford he had to go, with the pixies laughing in every hole and every rock up that unket cleeve. When he came out on Tarr Ball there right up ahead he saw the heifers, but when he gave chase the mist came down all round 'en.

And so it went on all night. He went down to Nutscale Brakes and out over Babe Hill and back again through the gorsey patch, and he couldn't get up with 'em. At last he gave up, and dragged himself home, all a-bruised and a-tore and soaked to the bare skin, and when he looked in over the barton door, there lay his four fine heifers fed and comfortable—and what's more they'd been there all night.

• 21 • *The Four-Eyed Cat*

Collected by Ruth L. Tongue in 1955 from N. Marchant, 12, daughter of a lightship sailor from Harwich and Dovercourt in Essex County. The girl heard the account from her grandparents.

Motifs here are G283.1.2.3, "Witch raises wind to sink ships of people who have injured her" and G211.1.7, "Witch in form of cat." Kittredge in Witchcraft in Old and New England, *chap. 8, "Wind and Weather," discusses witch powers to control the weather and call up storms.*

It is a general belief of fishermen all round the British Isles that it is unlucky to take a woman to the fishing grounds, and even unlucky to meet one on the way to sea. In some places the taboo extends to even mentioning a woman. Witch superstitions were rampant in Essex, and it is interesting to find them still surviving. The reference to "swimming" a witch is to a folk practice which found its way into witch trials in Scotland and England.

• THERE WAS A gentleman had a beautiful daughter who was bad at heart, and they said she knew more than a Christian should, and they wanted to swim her, but no one dared because of her father. She drew a spell on a poor fisherman, and he followed for love of her wherever she went. He deserted his troth-plight maid, though he was to be married in a week, and he ran away to sea with the gentleman's daughter and unbeknown to all the rest (that is, the rest of the fleet) took her out with them to the fishing. She did it to spite her father's pride, but he thought himself well rid of her.

A storm blew up and the whole fishing fleet were lost to a man for they had on board a woman with them at sea, though none knew of it but her lover. It was she that had whistled up the storm that had drowned her own lover, for she hated everyone. She was turned into a four-eyed cat, and ever after she haunted the fishing fleet.

So that is why even now fishermen won't cast their nets before half-past three (cock-crow)—my uncles won't—and they always throw a bit back into the sea for the cat.

•22• The Witch's Purse

Recorded from Mrs. Falconer, over 80, a lifelong resident of Leafield, Oxfordshire, August 8, 1962. The story was more lively

*and dramatic when she was not recording it on the tape, but even
in the recording the old witch's speeches were in more pro-
nounced dialect, and some attempt at dramatic impersonation
appeared in the telling.*

*Motifs present are B733.2, "Dog's howling ominous of death,"
discussed with classical references by T. F. Thiselton-Dyer,
English Folk-Lore (London, 1880), pp. 101–102; and G275.1,
"Devil carries off witch," treated by Kittredge,* Witchcraft in
Old and New England, *p. 43 and notes 164–67.*

• WHEN I WAS a little girl, my mother had a new baby, and of
course I was in the bedroom when this old lady came up in the
bedroom, and was talking to my mother, and then the dog
belonging to her began to howl. My mother was very concerned,
and she said, "Oh! do make that dog stop his noise. I hate to
hear a dog howl." Then this old lady said, "Let 'en 'owl, let 'en
'owl. 'E's 'owling arter that child." And 'er said, "Is anything
the matter with that child?" "No, not that I know, except that
it's going to die." And my mother was very concerned about it,
and it did die, it died when it was height days old. And of course
my mother was very concerned about it, and main frightened,
and she wouldn't let anyone go anywhere near for days, for
fear they'd tell her something to hurt this baby what was the
matter.

They went to Charlbury, which is ever so far, about four or
five miles, to fetch the doctor, to see if there was anything the
matter, and he said, "No, there's nothing the matter with it. No
earthly reason why it should die." But it did die, and that's all
I can tell you.

And some years after that, or some time after that, this old
lady did die, and my mother went in to look after her from next
door, and she said, "Rhoda, bring my purse off the table." And
my mother said, "Why do you want the purse for? You can't
spend money. You aren't able to get up."

"I wants my purse. You give it me. I can't open it. You open
it for me, and then I can manage." My mother opens this purse,
and there was a quantity of sovereigns in it. My mother saw them
quite plain, but she never counted 'em to know the quantity.

And she says, "Oh! That's all right. I shan't be here many more days." She counted 'em up. "My money'll last till then, and when that's gone," she says, "I shall go, because I'm not able to go to fetch any more."

And she did die, and when the daughter that belonged to this poor lady, the daughter, my mother said to her, "You'd better take care of that purse, because," she said, "I don't like being left alone with that purse. Because," she said, "your mother had it to look at, there's a lot of money in it. You take care of it."

And the old lady said, "Let it alone. Leave it there," and so they never moved it, and the daughter and my mother was there when she died. And when she died, and they'd done different things to her, like what they has to do, one of them saying, "You'd better take care of that purse, and see that's safe," they opened the purse, and there was nothink in it, it was quite empty. The Devil had took her and the money together.

· 23 · The Gipsy's Curse

Recorded from W. H. Barrett, resident of the Cambridgeshire Fens, on October 11, 1963. Mr. Barrett is the well-known story-teller who has published Tales from the Fens *and* More Tales from the Fens, *both edited by Enid Porter (London, 1963, 1964).*

Motif G269.4, "Curse by disappointed witch," is familiar in England and the United States. New England examples can be found in R. M. Dorson, Jonathan Draws the Long Bow *(Cambridge, Mass., 1946), pp. 33–35.*

Mr. Barrett writes in the course of a letter: "Everyone in those days that lived around my home held firm belief in the power witches possessed, and a lot of good food us children would have been glad to have was wasted by being placed outside the door for a wandering witch to collect for her supper, who never appeared in human form. Any seen were disguised as cats or rats, and it was a well-known fact the dish the food was placed

*in needed no washing up next morning, it was so clean. My
father, who was in great demand as a lay preacher in the Fen
chapels, firmly believed that stewed pigs' brains served on a plate
which had contained the witches' supper (unwashed) gave him
such power to preach in his sermons that it caused his listeners to
sit enthralled."*

• THERE WAS AN old gipsy woman who pitched her cariavan in a
waste piece of ground. She was a filthy old bitch, and we boys
used to be terrified to meet the glance of her deep-sunk dark
eyes. She'd set out every morning with a basket on her arm in
which there were pieces of dirty lace. This was really a legalized
form of begging. She would return home in the evening, with
the basket filled with what she had been given, scrounged, or
stolen. She was a terror to the people that lived close by, and
there was one woman whom—oh! she was always pestering;
eventually, the woman seemed on the verge of a nervous breakdown. So her husband went to the police, and asked the police if
they could not take the old gipsy's cariavan away. The police said
they could not, as it stood on waste ground, but they would send
along and warn the old gipsy that if she didn't stop pestering the
local people, they would put a pair of handcuffs on her, take
her before the magistrates, and have her sent to prison. Well, the
policeman went and warned the old gipsy.

That night, when the man who had been to the police was
returning from his work, the old gipsy stopped him on the high
road, and after spitting in his face, said, "Oh! You are the old
man who went and told the police to have me locked up and
sent to jail, are you? Well, you're a wicked old man, treating a
poor old woman like me like that. Now, in return for doing this,
I will give you a gipsy's curse; and that curse is, that neither
you, or any of your offspring will die in their own beds."

The man, being of a religious turn of mind, only shrugged
his shoulders, but there were some bystanders near. They'd heard
the gipsy curse him, but they forgot all about it until, some time
later, that man died at his work-bench, in his carpenter's shop.
As the years passed, five of his offspring died also, four in hos-
pital and one killed on active service. That makes you think a bit,

doesn't it? I have given a lot of thought to it myself, for, you see, the man on whom the gipsy laid her curse, was my father.

·24· *The Open Grave*

Contributed by Ruth L. Tongue to Folk-Lore, *LXXIII (1962), 106–108 as she heard it in Taunton Deane in 1961 and again in Chipstable in April, 1963, both in Somerset.*

Motifs here are K1601, "Deceiver falls into his own trap (literally)"; D1278.1, "Magic churchyard mould"; and C411.1, "Tabu: asking for reason of an unusual action." It is believed unlucky to leave a grave open on Sunday (E. and M. A. Radford, Encyclopedia *of Superstitions, p. 261); see the song in "Mr. Fox's Courtship" No. 43 in this volume.*

"Robin herdick" is a robin redbreast.

· THERE WAS A sexton who cared for a church, and he wasn't at all suitable. The parson was a rich hunting man, and there was very few services he troubled to hold, not more than two-three in the year. So sexton, he had his own way, and a bad way it was. Folk that were curious would notice him dig a grave, so of course they'd ask whose 'twas, and all he'd answer them was, "You'll see soon enough." And not a word more.

And sure enough, that open grave was filled with one of them. There were a godly and respected old farmer who was church-warden, and he had his doubts about sexton. One afternoon he came on him digging a grave, unbeknown to all, so he naturally asks whose 'tis. Sexton looked at him squinty-eyed, and says, "You'll know soon enough," and not a word more. And in three days farmer himself were buried in it.

By and by, folks came to notice that it were those who doubted the sexton as filled his open graves, but what to do about it they couldn't tell. Then old Betty, the gifted woman, she was guided to find a way. She came upon sexton in the dimmet, busy digging a new open grave, and she made a criss-cross avore she spoke a word, and she did not waste questions to put herself in his power

—no—she pick up a bit of grave-mould, and creeps up all on her tip-toes, and drops 'en down on sexton a-digging. "Hungry earth must be fed, and open graves lie in wait," says she. "You'll see soon enough."

Sexton, he let out a skritch like the foul fiend himself, and he began to climb out arter old Betty, but her skittered off, spry as a robin herdick, and he took and slipped on grave-edge, and a-fell onto his back-spine into 'en. Then he gave out two more fearsome yells. "Dree on 'en," says old Betty. "Aye, he can bide still now."

And there wasn't a sound in graveyard, but a whisper of wind in the grasses. Old Betty, she says her prayers and go on whoame, and sexton he lay there with his back a-broked. Come morning, folks could a-see his dead corpse in the open grave, and they all zee who 'twas vor soon enough.

My great-gran she did zay, "An open grave must be ved, or the man who digs it will find himself be one to fill it—in a coffin."

• 25 •   *Annie Luker's Ghost*

Recorded from Ruth L. Tongue, September 27, 1963, to whom the experience was told in 1963 in Somerset by the widow of the old man in the story, who more than hinted that her husband was a witch as well.

Relevant motifs are E401.1.2, "Footsteps of invisible ghost heard" (many references in E. W. Baughman, A Type and Motif-Index of the Folktales of England and North America) *and E247, "Ghost kills man who had had ghost exorcised for too short a time," for which Baughman cites a 1904 reference from Northumberland. The belief that a ghost will come to fetch one of the living away is fairly widespread, but perhaps best known in the corpse-candle beliefs investigated by Richard Baxter and John Aubrey in the seventeenth century (see Baxter,* The Certainty of the World of Spirits, *London, 1691 and Aubrey,* Miscellanies upon Various Subjects, *5th ed., London, 1890, pp. 165–67, "Corps-Candles in Wales"). The accusation*

*of taking the form of a rabbit or hare is commonly leveled
against witches in England (G211.2.7).*

· I KNOW WHAT you say about ghosts is quite true. We 'ad one to
our cottage. Oh, yes! We come down to cottage arter it were
empty, like, and I got Vicar to come and bless cottage. You see,
it did belong to old Annie Luker, and she wasn't well liked.
Everybody said she 'ad dark dealings; could turn 'erself into a
rabbit. Well, arter she died, there weren't no one as 'ud go near.
But my 'usband 'e was a clever man, bit too clever, if you ask
me, 'e say, "We'll go to cottage." So us took it.

Folk in village didn't like it very much, and they come and
say to me, "Does 'ee know 'twas Annie Luker's cottage?"

I says, "Yes, I'll get Vicar to come and bless it."

So we did, and we went there, me and my 'usband, and our
daughter Mary. Well, us 'ad been there about three months,
when all of a sudden, one night, I 'ears a girt bang. I sits up in
bed, and I listens, and someone come in! I could 'ear 'en downstairs. I nudges 'usband, see.

"Bob," I says, "wake up, will 'ee? What be it?"

Well, we sat up in bed, and then we could 'ear someone coming
upstairs—bump, bump, and kerflop, kerflop.

'Usband, 'e got proper cross, and 'e calls out, "Mary, what be
'ee about? Coming in this time o' night!"

Then us 'eard our Mary, from 'er bedroom next to ours, by
the passage-way, and she say, "Dad, oh! Dad, I've been 'ome
hours. Whatever is it?" And then 'er goes under blankets like
I did.

My 'usband 'e listened, and then we 'eard 'en again, thump,
thump, kerflop, kerflop coming along up the stairs towards our
door, and all of a sudden, my 'usband—'oo nothing much
worried 'im—'e say, "Oh! 'Tis old Annie Luker!" And 'e come
under blankets too.

Well, sometimes she'd come and sometimes she 'ouldn't. Never
see 'er, but 'ear 'er, yes. And then, my 'usband, 'e was took ill,
and not long ago 'e died. 'Aven't 'eard Annie since. Folks say
she knew what she wanted, and she come for 'im.

· 26 · The Son Murdered by His Parents

Printed by Myra E. Jennings in Old Cornwall, *II, No. 7 (Summer 1934, issued by the Federation of Old Cornish Societies), 40–41, with the comment, "This story was told by my great-grandfather to my mother, who told it to me."*

This is Type 939A, Killing the Returned Soldier, with a dramatic and logical addition of ghostly motifs: E451.4.1, "Ghost asked to identify self 'in name of God'"; E441, "Ghost laid by reburial"; and E4231.5, "Revenant as swine." Type 939A is sparsely reported from eastern Europe, but Maria Kosko has accumulated numerous variant texts; preliminary studies are her "Varia à propos du Malentendu," Comparative Literature, X (1958), 367–77, and "L'Auberge de Jérusalem à Dantzig," Fabula, IV (1961), 81–97. Her forthcoming monograph will devote two chapters to the fortunes of the legend in England. Baughman cites additional texts: from Michigan (Polish), in R. M. Dorson, "Polish Tales from Joe Woods," Western Folklore, VIII (1949), 136; from Missouri, in Vance Randolph, Who Blowed Up the Church House?, pp. 23–24, "The Boy that Fooled his Folks"; and from Cornwall, in Robert Hunt, Popular Romances of the West of England, 2nd series (London, 1865), pp. 253–55, "The Penryn Tragedy."

Literary uses of the theme appear in the play by George Lillo, The Fatal Curiosity (1736), the novel by Constance Holme, The Splendid Fairing (1933), and the humorous story by Stephen Leacock, "Caroline's Christmas" (1911), a comic reshaping of the tale.

· A WAYSIDE COTTAGE had belonged to two old people, who died, leaving it in very bad repair. Their only son had gone out, years before, to Australia, and no word had been heard from him since. So, after some time the cottage was done up, and new tenants moved in.

They found it impossible to live there though, because of

the strange sounds they heard at night. So badly was it haunted that the parson was called in. His efforts were all in vain and it remained empty.

Then one day an old stranger woman came through the village selling brooms, and hearing of the haunted house, she offered to lay the spirit herself; all she asked was a fire in the room, a table and a chair, a Bible, and some sewing to busy her hands with. These she was gladly given, and she settled down to keep her lonely watch.

At midnight the door burst open, and in lurched—a monstrous pig! Laying her hand on the Holy Book, the old woman said, "Satan, depart, and let this spirit come back in its natural form." On this, the pig went out and a young man came in its place. And when told to "Speak in God's name," this is the story he told.

He was the missing son of the old people who had lived there. Out in Australia he had fallen on bad times, and for lack of any good news to send, he had not written home for years. Suddenly he struck gold, and having made his fortune, he decided to come home and give his parents a joyful surprise. He arrived at the town near his old home, too late to bank his money as he had intended, and took it with him as he walked out to his parents' cottage. When he got there and found that he had altered so much that his own parents did not recognize him, he carried on the joke, as he thought, by asking and obtaining a night's lodging, and listening over a scanty supper to their tale of poverty and distress. He went to bed, glad in his heart to think of the grand sensation he would cause when he revealed himself and his riches to them in the morning. But the old people, poor wretches, were even more desperate than he had realized. Somehow they had caught the gleam, and felt the weight of his gold, and falling under the dreadful temptation, they killed "the stranger" in his sleep, and buried him behind the house.

"Come," said the spirit, "and see where my bones lie. Let them be gathered, and laid in consecrated ground, and I will trouble this place no more." The old woman followed, and the spirit hovered over one particular spot in the garden, and then disappeared. Fearing lest she should not recognize the exact place by daylight, she took off the thimble which she was still wearing, and with it marked the place. Next day the ground was dug over, bones were found there and duly buried in the churchyard, after which the cottage remained as quiet at night as any other.

•27• *Company on the Road*

Recorded from Fred Bayliss in Burford, Oxfordshire, November 11, 1963. Mr. Bayliss's father had various other ghostly experiences, which he told to his children. The family is one of those distinguished by a death warning. There are a great many ghostly legends in the neighbourhood of Burford.

Motifs present are E422.1.1.4, "Headless ghost carries head under arm"; E332.2, "Person meets ghost on road"; and E587.5, "Ghost walks at midnight." For the striking first motif Baughman gives references to instances from Yorkshire, Shropshire, Somerset, Lincolnshire, and from Massachusetts.

The Sarsden Stones are a pair of fine ornamental stone gateposts, of late seventeenth-century style, which stand on each side of a track to Churchill on the Chipping Norton road.

• WELL, IT WAS roughly at the turn of the century that my father courting my mother—my father living in Chipping Norton, and my mother at Milton-under-Wychwood—used to walk the six miles there and back, every Wednesday and Saturday, coming back early on Wednesday, but always leaving it till midnight on the Saturday. And just at the point of the road where he'd often heard what appeared to be a coach and horses go roaring across, through the Sarsden Pillars and on down through the drive, he always felt he'd like to come across a fellow traveler, especially on the dark nights. And then, one night, he realized that he'd someone walking by the side of him, and being dark, he never bothered to look round, but started talking, and was quite happily talking away, never realizing that he was not actually getting any reply or conversation from the other person. And this happened on two dark nights.

And then the third night, when he was going along, it was almost full moon, and he never bothered to look round, as usual, and started talking, and then the fact that he wasn't getting any replies made him look round all of a sudden. And what he had walking by the side of him was a headless Elizabethan gentleman, with his head tucked tightly under his right arm. This, of course, thoroughly upset my father, and he took to his heels and fled as far as Downs Hollow cottages, where he took refuge. And I'm afraid after that, my father changed the time he was walking along the road, and made quite sure he wasn't passing the Sarsden Pillars later than eleven o'clock at night. And that actually was the last time he saw the apparition.

· 28 · *Room for One More*

Heard by Katharine M. Briggs about 1912 as a child in Dunkeld, Perthshire, from a visitor who lived in London. This is an urban, not a regional legend. A folder in the Indiana University Folklore Archives, titled "Urban Belief Tale: Room for One More," contains five texts, four collected in Michigan and one in Minnesota. The setting of the story is usually in a large city, such as Chicago, New York, or Detroit.

Motif D1810.8.3.2, "Dream warns of danger which will happen in near future," is reported by Baughman for England, Scotland, and the United States. Also relevant is E723, "Wraiths of persons separate from body."

There were recently stories extant in Perth of people who were warned by a dream and put off their journey, thus escaping the disaster when the newly made Tay Bridge broke and the train was hurled into the Firth of Tay on December 28, 1879.

· A YOUNG WOMAN on her way up to town broke her journey by staying with friends at an old manor house. Her bedroom looked out to the carriage sweep at the front door. It was a moonlight night, and she found it difficult to sleep. As the clock outside her bedroom door struck twelve, she heard the noise of horses' hoofs on the gravel outside, and the sound of wheels. She got up and went over to the window, to see who could be arriving at that time of night. The moonshine was very bright, and she saw a hearse drive up to the door. It hadn't a coffin in it; instead it was crowded with people. The coachman sat high up on the box; as he came opposite to the window he drew up and turned his head. His face terrified her, and he said in a distinct voice, "There's room for one more." She drew the curtain close, and ran back to bed, and covered her head with the bedclothes. In the morning she was not quite sure whether it had been a dream, or whether she had really got out of bed and seen the hearse, but she was glad to go up to town and leave the old house behind her.

It was a shopping expedition she was going on, and she was shopping in a big store which had a lift in it—an up-to-date thing at that time. She was on the top floor, and she went to the lift to go down. It was rather crowded, but as she came up, the lift-man turned his head, and said, "There's room for one more." It was the face of the coachman of the hearse. "No, thank you," said the girl, "I'll walk down." She turned away, the lift doors clanged, there was a terrible rush and screaming and shouting, and then a great clatter and thud. The lift had fallen from the top to the bottom of the building and every soul in it was killed.

•29• *The Giant of Grabbist and the "Dorcas Jane"*

Recorded from Ruth L. Tongue, September 23, 1963, as she recalled childhood memories of the tradition in Somerset, 1908–25. Tellers of the tradition were a farmer near Dunster, an Exmoor blacksmith, and a friend from Watchet.

The benevolent giant is not unknown in folklore but is rather rare. The international tale-type nearest to this in mood is 701, The Giant's Toy Returned, best known in Sweden and Slovenia. Pertinent motifs are F531.3.9, "Giants sit on mountains to wash

*their feet in a stream"; F531.3.1, "Giant wades the ocean";
and N812, "Giant or ogre as helper." All are found in Scandinavian and Germanic tradition.*

• WE 'AVEN'T GOT many giants about at Zummerzet, I 'ear, but
we 'ave one down to Dunster. Ah! Come up from Cornwall, 'e
did, and 'e didn't like staying in Devon, 'cos 'is cousins there were
a bit rough like. 'E come up to Exmoor, nice peaceful friendly
place it is. But the folk on Exmoor, they didn't like size
of 'im; bit scared they was. But then they found out that there
wasn't no sheepstealers round about, cattle and sheep was thriv-
ing, and 'e didn't 'arm no one. They got quite fond of 'im. And
then farmers' wives they began to put their heads together.
"Whatever did the poor girt veller veed on?"

Well, I think they was all quite ready to go and cook a dinner
for 'im, but they found they needn't. You see, word come up
from Yarnton as 'e were fond o' fish; 'e did take and wade out
down channel, right out to sea, and all the fishing boats 'ad to do
was to follow 'en. Oh! they come out o' Minehead 'arbor, loaded,
they did, all the fishing boats, right up Bristol way, to Portishead,
and 'e'd go and 'e'd wade out there, and water'd come up to 'is
armpits, and 'e'd scoop up girt shoals o' fish, and 'twas a wonder-
ful time for the fishing boats.

Well now, one time, old 'Lijah Crowcombe and 'is crew from
the "Dorcas Jane," they'd managed to catch up. Oh! she were a
leaky old craft were the "Dorcas Jane," and they was loaded
right up and 'er were a-wallowing in the waves when a storm
comes up. Well, all craft ran for it, and they thought they were
going down to bottom, when through the storm, and all the wind
and the mist, the giant comes a-striding, and 'e picks up "Dorcas
Jane," and afore they could say "Thank 'ee," 'e puts 'er down
quiet and safelike, in Watchett 'arbor. Then off and away 'e go,
back to Dunster.

Well, Dunster folk got quite fond 'o 'im arter that, and they'd
wait to wave to 'en when 'en came back from the sea. 'E come up
along by the river, and 'e'd sit on the 'ill, with 'is feet on either
side 'o the castle, and wash the mud off 'is legs in the river
Laune. Then off and away 'e'd go, on up the 'ill, and folks used

to look out of their windows to wave to 'en, and 'e'd wave back, and there was all the week's washing—dried!

• 30 • The Giant of Grabbist and Hawkridge Church

Recorded by Ruth L. Tongue September 29, 1963, who heard the Somerset story at Exford in the Dulverton area in the 1920's from an old hunt servant, aged about 75; from a farm laborer, aged about 60, at Wilmersham, in 1930; and from a thatcher, aged about 60, from Porlock, in 1940.

The motif of the friendly giant bringing stones to build a church is unusual, but it is listed by Evald Tang Kristensen in Danske Sagn *(1895), Vol. III, A5, who cites 12 instances. See also R. Th. Christiansen,* The Migratory Legends, *5020, "Ferrying Troll Across a Lake. Troll Making a causeway," for legends of trolls causing remarkable formations of stones. In the 20 Cornish legends of "The Giants" given by Robert Hunt,* Popular Romances of the West of England, *First Series (London, 1865), pp.3–61, stone and boulder formations are constantly attributed to acts of giants.*

Applicable motifs are F531.3.2.1, "Church built where giants throw stones"; and A977.1, "Giant responsible for certain stones."

• WELL NOW, THE giant, 'e were very 'appy to Exmoor, and then the Old Gentleman, 'e decided 'e'd better come back. 'E didn't like seeing they little thatched churches going up all over the way. So when the folk of 'Awkridge thought they'd build theirselves a church, eight hundred feet up 'tis, the Old Man didn't like it, and then 'e found giant were 'elping. Ah! so Old Nicky, 'e tried to trip giant up. Giant were coming across by Spire Cross, wi' a load o' girt stones, and 'e tripped, and they went all abroad.

Well, giant didn't say nothing, 'e didn't lose 'is temper, as

Old Nicky 'oped 'e would, and cause a storm. No, 'e just patiently bent, and 'e pick 'em up, one arter another, and 'e put 'em up on 'Awkridge for church. And then 'e came to a girt broken one, and 'e tossed 'en aside into the very wood where the Old Boy were a-sitting, chuckling, and that made 'en go off in a hurry. And 'e picks up the rest of the stones, as weren't no good for church, and 'e laid 'en across the stream, the river Barle it is, and there 'e made Tarr Steps.

·31· *The Giant of Grabbist and the Whitstones*

Recorded from Ruth L. Tongue, September 28, 1963, who heard the Somerset legend of Hurlstone Point and the Whitstones of Bossington Wood from the following persons all, save the last, over 60: John Ash, carter, working at East Lucott in 1941; Mr. Keal, a farmer, on East Lucott Farm, 1941; Mrs. Stenner, cottager, Porlock area, 1944; Walter Badcock, coach driver, Minehead, 1952; Miss Brown of Bessington, 1959.

The contest of the giant and the Devil is unusual; customarily a hero outwits giant, Devil, or ogre. E. T. Kristensen lists a stone-throwing contest between giants, Danske Sagn, Vol. III, A4, No. 93. Motifs are F531.3.2, "Giant throws a great rock," and A977.2, "Devil throws stones."

A "sucker" is a young foal, "zogs" is bogland.

· WELL, THE GIANT 'e made up 'is mind as there wasn't room for 'e and Old Nicky up on moor, and Old Nicky, 'e just about made up 'is mind the same. Now you see, the giant, 'e liked St. Dubricius and all they little churches, so 'e and Old Nicky, they got together, Porlock way, and they said they'd have a competition like. They'd each throw a big stone from Bossington Beacon over to Porlock Common, that be four miles, and 'ooever lost 'ud 'ave to leave the place for good and all.

Well, Old Nick 'ad first throw and 'is stone, 'e flew out over the four mile, and 'e landed up on Porlock Common. And then, just afore giant were a-going to throw 'is, Old Nick, 'e trip 'im up, and giant's stone, 'e fell down about three feet away from where Old Nick's was; but 'e didn't go away. No, 'e just trip up Old Nick 'isself, and 'e sat on 'en; right down on 'en 'e sat. There's some folks say 'e just smoked a pipe, quiet-like, and Old Nick 'e just squirmed round underneath, but no! When giant had finished 'is pipe, then 'e pick up Old Nick by 'is tail, and 'e say, "That wasn't a fair throw. We'll throw from Quantock later on. Meantime, you go cool your head." And 'e toss Old Nick up in the air, and 'e throw 'im right out down Channel, out over Porlock Bay, and then 'e smiled to 'isself, and 'e come away over the moor, quite 'appy like, till 'e got to Cottishead Moor, and there 'e found a poor little sucker, as 'ad got 'isself a-zinking in the zogs there, an' 'is little brown mother was a-crying for 'elp piti-ful. Well, giant picked the silly little thing out, and 'e rub 'im down very gentle, with 'is girt finger, and 'e put 'en down by 'is little brown mother, and away 'e went.

·32· *The Giant of Grabbist and the Stones of Battlegore*

Recorded from Ruth L. Tongue, September 28, 1963, as she heard the account from Walter Badcock in Minehead. This is the end of the preceding Somerset legend.

· OUR OLD GIANT and Old Nick, they did meet arter a while, on the Quantock Hills, up by West Quantock 'twas, and they was to throw their stones, and this time the giant was ready for Old Nicky, and afore 'e could do anything, giant 'ad picked up 'is stone, and throwed right over to Battlegore, six miles away. "Your turn now," 'e say.

Old Nicky were dancing wi' rage, and I think 'e were so cross about 'en, that 'is stone fell down, and the giant's was the furthest off. "Now," says the giant, "'tis your promise to go

away from round here, and never come back no more. But as no
one don't trust you, I'll make sure." And 'e pick up Old Nicky
by 'is tail, and 'e wade out down the Severn Channel, till 'e were
right out to the sea, 'twere up to 'is armpits. And then 'e give
'im a good swing, three times round 'is head, and let go. Well,
I reckon the Old Un landed somewhere about the West Indies;
anyway, 'e get a good long swim back.

'E's back o' course, but 'e don't shew 'isself in Zummerzet,
'case the giant be about.

·33· St. Wulfric and the Greedy Boy

*Recorded from Ruth L. Tongue, September 29, 1963, who heard
the tradition as a child at Hazelbury Plucknett in Somerset.*

*Miss Tongue comments: "I was told this tale, which I can
remember verbatim, by an old Somerset retired clergyman of 83.
He told it to me every time I asked for it, which was often. I was
five, and when he was five he heard it from his great-grandmother, who was over seventy when she came to see him, and
she heard it from her great-grandmother. 'When she was five?'
I asked, thrilled by this real traditional tale. 'Very likely, my dear
little trot,' he answered. So at a rough estimate we reach back
from me in 1963 to approximately 1681, before Sedgemoor."*

*Prominent motifs here are Q45.1.3, "Hospitality to saint
repaid"; V411.6, "Food given away by saint miraculously
restored"; and Q552.3.5, "Punishment for greed." Walter de la
Mare has very well retold the theme in his notes to* Come Hither
(New York, 1923), p. 540.

*"Teddies" are potatoes; "a dew-bit" is an early morning snack;
"drashel" is threshold.*

• THERE WAS A poor widow with a large family and they all
worked hard, even the little ones, and folk were very kind. There
was always an egg or two or a sack of teddies, or a cabbage, or a
bit of bacon put by to help them out. Then the farmers found
work and their food for the biggest lads, and they ought to have

managed, but they all went on looking so thin as a yard of pump
water except Dicky—and he grew fat. One day the poor widow
crept to St. Wulfric's cell. She'd brought him a thin little flat
oat loaf, made from the scrapings of the meal chest. St. Wulfric
took it and the three little trots that had come with their mother
burst into tears as they saw it go.

The saint looked down at their poor little pinched faces, and
whispered gently, "Go down to the spring for me, and see what
the birds have left me." So off they toddled—half the size of the
pail the baby was—but he would go. And back they staggered
with it only half full, their poor little sticks of arms and legs
couldn't lift more. But the baby's face was rosy with joy over a
big loaf with fresh butter, and a crock of cream they'd found
there.

"Now, sit down and eat them," said the saint, "my birds must
have known you were coming. But I've a use for your mother's
oat cake." Down they sat in the sunshine, and down the good
food went—and after that it was easy for the grateful widow to
tell her troubles.

" 'Tis our Dicky, zur, he do get his vittles all down to Varmer
Mellish where he be bird boy, and they do give he a-plenty. But
never were such a boy to eat, Missus Mellish say, and they be
hearty trenchermen down there. But when he do come whoame
a-night he do gollop up all in the house if I don't stop him. Then
he do sneaky round when alls asleep and there's nought for
breakfusses. *And* he do get his dew-bit at farm, no fear! All my
others, they do bring a few bits of vittles whoame for me and
they little trots, but if Dicky be about 'tis all goed down his
throat while they be getting two bites in—and him so fat as a
pig!"

"Tell him I want to see him," said the saint. So after they'd
picked the saint a bunch of primroses, and he'd blessed them,
she took the little trots home. They even ran a bit. Next day, a
fat sulky lad came to the cell. "I want you to take any bread
you see on my shelf down to your mother," said the saint. "Be
very quiet, for it is time I was at my prayers."

Dicky glanced at the shelf and saw his mother's oat cake. He'd
searched for it all night! And she'd given it to an old man who

knelt on a cold stone floor—the old fool! Here he looked at the shelf again and there were two large white cottage loaves beside the oat cake. Dicky grabbed them in terror and ran for it, scared out of his wits. He was so fat he soon lost his breath, and sat down on the turf—and the loaves smelt delicious. Nobody would know what happened to them. The silly old saint was busy praying and his mother wouldn't expect any food. Down Dicky's red lane went all three loaves, yes, oat cake and all, and my young raskill strolls off home. He wasn't feeling at all happy inside and there were no end of queer pains so he didn't go indoors but sat down on the drashel. Out came his mother smiling and handed him a big crust of white bread covered with butter.

"There, Dicky," she said, "you shall have a taste for being such a good, kind boy, bringing in they three loaves from the saint. Lovely bread 'tis, like us ate yesteddy, I did wish you others could taste."

But Dicky's hair was standing on end. "T-three?" he gasped.

"A girt big oat cake and two white loaves all a-buttered," she said, "I did find they on table where you did a-put them."

With that Dicky took off in terror and never stopped till he got back to the saint's cell. St. Wulfric was still kneeling, and there on the shelf above him were a poor thin little oat cake and two cottage loaves. Dicky stood there and shook with fear.

Then St. Wulfric stood up, "You must be hungry after your climb," he said. "Finish your bread and butter." Dicky dare not refuse, but, oh, how terrible it was. It left him with such a taste in his mouth that he didn't eat for days—until he was as thin as the baby had been. After that he never made fun of saints or took more than his share. He even brought his mother home *three* eggs one evening!

·34· The Devil and St. Dunstan

Collected by Ruth L. Tongue in Glastonbury, Somerset, in the summer of 1946, from an old farmer near Glastonbury. Later the same year she heard another version from a farm laborer at Street while he was taking his nummet (midday snack).

Motifs here are T332, "Man tempted by fiend in woman's shape," and G303.9.4.4, "Devil tempts cleric (hermit)."

Saint Dunstan (A.D. 924–88) was one of the great churchmen of the Anglo-Saxon Church. A reputation for occult powers hovered about him from the beginning of his career. When he was quite a boy and only a lay churchman he had to purge himself of an accusation of black magic by the water ordeal, which in those days was the opposite of the later swimming of a witch. When he had been converted by St. Alphege and was living a life of great austerity many tales began to be told of his personal encounters with the Devil. The Somerset tale belongs to the time when he was Abbot of Glastonbury, in the reign of King Edmund. The better known version of the story, however, belongs to the time when he was Archbishop of Canterbury and had a palace at Mayfield in Sussex. It seems to be an historical fact that St. Dunstan, as well as being skilled in music and painting, was an accomplished blacksmith. Ecclesiastically one of his great concerns was with the celibacy of the clergy, so that it is appropriate that St. Dunstan should triumph over the Devil in the form of a woman. In the Mayfield version of the story the Devil is said to have flown over to Tunbridge Wells after he had been released, where he cooled his nose in the springs, which ever after had a sulfurous taste and a reddish tinge. The tongs with which the Devil's nose was pinched are still preserved in Mayfield Palace.

Hilaire Belloc retells a similar story pleasantly in The Four Men: A Farrago *(London, 1902), pp. 31–42; the Devil fails to finish his ditch before dawn, and has his nose pinched by tongs.*

• THE OLD BOY were out looking for mischief when he come by Glastonbury. Says he, "I'll have that St. Dunstan tonight, never mind how." He'd had a two–three tries before, but he would be bound he'd get him some time. He hears a hammering in the saint's cell, and he takes a squint in, and there's St. Dunstan, who was a handy man with tools, amusing hisself beating out a gold

chain. The Old Boy turns hisself into a beautiful young lady
and come a-sidling in through door.

"Is that for me?" he says in a voice so sweet as a song thrush
after rain. Now, St. Dunstan don't like beautiful young ladies
anyhow, and this one's got a gurt ox-hoof peeping out under her
frock. He don't look up, see, but he goes on a-blowing pincers
red-hot. The Old Boy, he sidles nearer, and gives him a loving
look from eyes so bright as morning dew, and St. Dunstan he
still goes on blowing. Then he turns round all on a sudden, and
there! he'd a-got the Old Boy's purty nose nipped atween the
white-hot tongs. I reckon he kept away from Glastonbury after
that.

· 35 · St. Adelme

*From John Aubrey's manuscript on Wiltshire, Hypomnemata
Antiquaria A (Bodleian MS Aubrey 3). Aubrey heard the tradition in 1645 from old Ambrose Brown at Malmesbury.*

*Motifs present are T540.1, "Supernatural birth of saints";
D2122.5, "Journey with magic speed by saint"; and
D2072.0.2.2.1, "Person charged with keeping birds from crops
confines them in barn." E. M. Butler in* The Myth of the Magus
*(New York, 1948), discusses spirits who perform at various
speeds, including one quick as thought selected by Faust to serve
a banquet, and also describes magic objects enabling Faust to fly
through the air (pp. 127–40). Legends of Merlin's miraculous
birth are given on pp. 105–106.*

For ringing of bells to avert thunder and lightning see Handwörterbuch des deutschen Aberglaubens, *V, 939.*

*It seems that people of outstanding sanctity can not only con-
trol devils but may even employ their services without danger.*

· St. Adelme, Abbot of Malmesbury; his father was a weaver,
who as he rose early to go to worke, walking over the churchyard, when he came to the crosse something frightened him still.
He spoke to his wife to go along with him; she did, and when

she came to the crosse she was struck at the bottome of her belly, and conceived this Saint.

Miracle. When a boy—one Sundaye as they were at Masse he filled a barn full of little birds.

This Saint gave a bell to the Abbey, which when it was rung, had the power to make the thunder and lightning cease.

The Pope, hearing of his Fame, sent for him to preach at Rome: he had not above two daies warning to goe. Wherefore he conjured for a fleet spirit. Up comes a spirit he asks how fleet. resp: as fleet as a bird in the air. yt was not enough. Another as fleet as an arrow out of a bow. not enough either. a 3rd as swift as thought. This would do. He commands it to take the shape of a horse, and presently it was so; a black horse on which his great saddle and footcloth was putt.

The first thing he thought on was St Pauls steeple lead: he did kick it with his foot and asked where he was, and the spirit told him, etc. When he came to Rome the groom asked what he should give his horse quoth he, a peck of live coales.

This from an old man at Malmesbury.

·36· *St. Aloys and the Lame Nag*

Recorded from Ruth L. Tongue, September 29, 1963, as she heard it from a carter at Wincanton in Somerset, where the legend is well known.

There is a carving of St. Aloys at Wincanton Church. There is also a very fine alabaster carving in the Nottingham Castle Museum representing the miracle. St. Aloys was not St. Aloysius Gonzaga but the earlier St. Eligius of Noyon. Sabine Baring-Gould says in his Lives of the Saints (XV, p. 9), *"In art he is represented erroneously as a farrier, with a horse's leg in his hand; the story going that as he was one day shoeing a horse, the animal proved restive, so he took the leg off, shod it, and put it on again, without evil consequences."*

The story is known in France and Germany and is discussed

by P. Saintyves in his Saints, Successeurs des Dieux (Paris, 1907),
pp. 248–51.

Type 753, Christ and the Smith, popular throughout Europe,
uses Motif E782.4, "Horse's leg cut off and replaced," present
here, but with the sequel of a disastrous attempt at imitation.
A Kentucky text is in Marie Campbell, Tales from the Cloud
Walking Country (Bloomington, Indiana, 1958), pp. 191–93,
"The Blacksmith That Tried Doctoring."

• THERE WERE A carter 'ad a 'oss. Fine 'oss 'e were, worked wonderful till 'e took 'en carting stones, and they broked 'is feet
dreadful. 'E 'ad a sand-crack so wide you could 'a' put a finger
in it. Well! when 'e took 'en down to blacksmith, 'e couldn't
do nothing for it. 'Ot as fire that foot was, and the butcher 'e
began to get 'is axe ready. But the carter, 'e was proper proud o'
that 'orse, real fond of it 'e was, so 'e 'ears about St. Aloys, down
to Wincanton, and 'e reckoned as 'ow 'e'd take cart'orse there.
Well, it took 'en the best part o' two days to do the two mile, but
carter 'e were determined 'oss should 'ave a chance. Well, when
they got to Wincanton, St. Aloys come out of 'is smithy. "Bring
'oss in 'ere," says 'e, "I'll take care of 'en, and 'ere's a bit o'
zider for 'ee, and some bread and cheese." "I'm feared 'e won't
stand," says carter, knowing 'ow 'e'd treated blacksmith. "Oh!
'E'll be all right," says St. Aloys.

So carter, 'e sits down to 'ave 'is zider, and 'is bread and cheese;
welcome as May, it was; and Saint, 'e just put 'is 'and on old
'oss, and then 'e go into smithy. Carter, 'e took a look, and then
'e took another look, and 'e gollops down 'is zider. There's old
'oss, wi' a bit o' 'ay in 'is mouth, what Saint 'ad give 'im, and
Saint were busy in the smithy, and old 'oss were standing there
wi' three legs!"

" 'Ere we are then," says the saint coming out, and 'e brings
out fourth leg, and 'e claps it on, and old 'oss stands there, and
'e nuckers quietly wi' 'is bit of 'ay. And 'e worked for years arter
that. Ah! That was St. Aloys, that was, down to Wincanton.
Proper fine smith!"

·37· St. David's Flood

Recorded from Ruth L. Tongue, September 9, 1963. This historical tradition is from the Blackdown Hills and a village called Thorn St. Margaret. It is about a village called Bleadon, and Miss Tongue has heard it many times in Somerset, first in 1906 and last in 1960. This version is from a farmer's daughter who used to hear the story from her grandfather. It contains Motif N825.3, "Old woman helper."

A tradition rather reminiscent of this is a Hampshire legend preserved in a poem by Charlotte M. Yonge, "The Cat of Cat Copse" (Monthly Packet, Christmas, 1879, p. 17), about a Saxon boy, a thane's son, who had been carried away by the Norsemen, whose boat was stranded by the tide as they sailed up a river for another raid. Like the Danes of Bleadon they were all massacred. The boy was left alone in the boat with the white kitten he had carried away with him. He escaped over the mud and hid in Catwood Copse while the slaughter of the Danes went on. The next day the cat led him back to his ruined home, where he found his father and King Alfred mourning the slaughter that the Danes had made.

Another Somerset tradition, commemorated in an early poem of Wordsworth, "The Danish Boy" (composed 1799), is of a Danish lad who was spared by the intercession of the Saxon women when a camp of the Danes was destroyed, and kept as a herd-boy. The ghosts of the boy and his dog are said to haunt the hill above, where he used to sit crooning Danish songs and looking over the sea.

"Hurd-yed" means red-head, and it is supposed to mean either Danish or pixy blood in Somerset.

• ST. DAVID'S FLOOD is a name for the spring tide which in the old days brought Christian saints to Somerset. They came up river on St. David's Flood. Later on there was a fishing hamlet down by the shore, and one day all the men were out fishing and a little herd boy came running back to the village in terror to say that six Danish galleys were sailing along and would come up the river on St. David's Flood. Well, the women and the children scampered away to the nearby village of Uphill, which could give them some safety, and they could warn the farming folk there. But one old granny was down by the riverside gathering gladdon for thatching her cottage, and as the long ships sailed by she crouched down among the rushes and watched the Danes landing and scattering to plunder. They had tied up their boats and left them without even a guard. St. David's Flood had brought them up, the very flood that had carried the saints up in olden days, but it was turning now, it was not waiting for the pirates to finish their work.

When they had gone the old woman crept out from her hiding place and watched the tide. It runs out very quickly there, and she saw that it was on the turn. So she undid the mooring of each of the galleys, and then she stood and watched them jostling against each other, going down river and out into the Severn Sea. In the meantime the men of Uphill had done their work well. They had ambushed the loaded pirates and driven them back towards their boats. But no boats were there, and not a hurd-yed survived that bloody day. And that, they say, is why the village is called Bleadon.

· 38 · The Legend of Gold Hill

Reprinted from W. H. Barrett, Tales from the Fens, *ed. Enid Porter (London: Routledge and Kegan Paul, 1963), pp. 133–35. Told to Barrett by his great-uncle, who lived near Gold Hill, in the Cambridgeshire Fens.*

An example of the racy and creative treatment of historical tradition by the English countrymen. Recognizable motifs are K331, "Goods stolen while owner sleeps"; K301, "Master thief"; K620, "Escape by deceiving the guard"; N765, "Meeting with robber band"; and F709.3, "Country of thieves."

Organized bands of thieves are prominent in Charles Dickens'

Oliver Twist (*1837*) *and Victor Hugo's* Notre Dame de Paris (*1831*).

· HUNDREDS OF YEARS ago King John, who had heard of the fine goings on at Wisbech Fair, thought he might have a bit of fun there himself, so he came to the castle, and put up there for the night. Then he joined the crowd at the Fair and made as much noise as anyone else. After the frolics were over, the king was just sober enough to find his own way back to the castle, taking a Wisbech wench with him to keep him warm from the cold fen wind. But when he woke up in the morning, he found that all his money and jewels were missing and that the girl had gone, and his servant too.

John flew into a terrible temper, and ordered the castle to be searched from top to bottom, but all that was found were six wenches from Wisbech down in the soldiers' quarters, and they swore they knew nothing of any jewels or treasures, they'd only come to the castle to do the weekly wash. So the king fretted and fumed and ordered the sentry who'd been on duty at the gate to be hung from the castle wall; then he clattered out of the castle, leaving orders that the search was to go on. No one remembered to change that order and that's why people are still looking for that treasure today.

Next morning a man came into the castle yard with his cart, to take the dung away from the stables, and he was just bending down to lift up a load, when a dagger was pushed between his ribs and he fell down dead. Then the king's servant and the girl who'd shared John's bed that night lifted up the corpse and dumped it in the cart. The girl nipped in beside it, and the servant pulled down the top. Then he led the horse to the castle gate, which the sentry unbolted for him, and came out on to the road and into the marketplace. There he took the horse out of the shafts and left the cart standing by the hot-eel stall. When the stall-holder came back from the tavern, not liking the smell of the dung in the cart, he put himself between the shafts and pulled the cart along to the river bank and toppled it into the river, where it sank.

Now as the servant and the girl were riding along on the horse, they were seen by two Fenmen who were lying hidden in the reeds near the trackway just outside Wisbech. By making the sound of bird calls, the two men passed on the news to others, hidden farther along the track, that two travelers were on their way. These others passed the message on until the servant and the girl had come to a group of huts standing hidden in tall reeds and osiers. A crowd of Fenmen were waiting for them here and they surrounded the pair and made them get off the horse. The servant knew that the men would recognize the livery he was wearing, so he told them that he and his wife were royal servants; they had lost their way, and were wandering along the track trying to find their master.

"And what have you got in those two leather bags?" asked the Fenmen. "Money," said the servant, "gold and silver money and a lot of jewels and precious stones which I stole last night from the king, when he was asleep." And he emptied out the bags to show his haul.

"Well," said the Fenmen, "we certainly don't want to kill a man who seems to be better than ten of us when it comes to thieving. So you'd better come here and live with us, there's plenty of work going in your trade with all the money that's lying about in the manors on the edge of the Fens."

So the man and the girl were taken to the mound where the Fenmen lived, and were given a hut and a cooking pot. They were also taught the law of the Fens, which was that they must never steal from a neighbor and must always help each other in time of need. They soon settled down in their new home and one of the first things they did was to pack up the royal livery inside the two leather bags, and send them by boat down to Lynn. From there the bags were sent on to the king, who, when he saw them, flew into such a rage that he had a fit and died. Then just nine months after Wisbech Fair, the girl had a lusty boy who, when he grew up, was called the Prince, and he became the greatest thief the Fens have ever known.

Meantime, of course, the Fenmen made the most of all the gold and silver coins which the servant and the girl had brought. Most of the money went on paying the Abbot of Ely so that the Fenmen he held in prison could be set free, and so much gold was paid out that the monks began to wonder where it all came from. But the Fenmen could never use the jewels, so they divided them among themselves, and each man hid his share under the floor of his hut. Years afterwards a great flood came and swept right over the Welney Fens and washed away all the huts. Later on the Dutchmen came, to drain the Fens and dig wide ditches, and one of these went right across the Fen, near where the huts had been. While they were working on the ditch, they came across a few pieces of jewelry, and later on a few more bits were turned up by the plough. When folks heard of this, they began to call the mound, where those old Fenmen had lived, "Gold Hill." So you see, John didn't lose all his treasures in the Wash; some of it disappeared at a place between Littleport and Wisbech, on the Welney Wash.

•*39*•   *The Grey Goose Feathers*

Recorded from W. H. Barrett, October 11, 1963. Mr. Barrett heard this tradition of the Cambridgeshire Fens from Chafer Legge in 1900. His written version, edited by Enid Porter, is in Tales from the Fens *(London, 1963), pp. 148–49, and is close to the oral text. The grey goose feathers also enter into another unusual tradition in the same book, "French Prisoners in the Fens," pp. 73–84.*

Identifiable motifs are M202.0.1, "Bargain or promise to be fulfilled at all hazards"; M205, "Breaking of promises or bargains"; and K1812, "King in disguise."

• THOUSANDS AND THOUSANDS of years ago, the Fenmen, living in their desolate wastes, bonded themselves into a secret society. This society was called "The Brotherhood of the Grey Goose Feathers," and anyone who was initiated into that brotherhood, and possessed a grey goose feather, was sure that whenever they was in trouble or distress, help would immediately be given by the whole Fenmen. When King Charles the First escaped from

Oxford, he made his way into the uplands of Norfolk, and stayed at a place called Stowe Hall, just outside of Downham Market.

And in passing, I may remark that I saw the chamber where, in case Cromwell's men came to look for him, he did hide. This chamber was aside of a great big chimney; it was hidden by old paneling.

Well, after Charles had consulted with his advisers, he decided to rejoin his troops just outside Oxford. The safest route in those days, for a fugitive, was through the desolate trackless Fens. There was one man, named Porter, who kept an inn at Southery. He used to guide travelers across the trackless waste. So he was sent for, and asked if he would take a very important personage to Huntingdon, and he said, "Yes, I will." So they brought the important personage to see what sort of a man the old Fenman was, and some of the King's advisers didn't think it was safe for him to go that long journey with only one man. But Porter said if that was what was worrying them, he would initiate the important personage into the Brotherhood of the Grey Goose Feathers. So they brought a feather, and Porter severed it down the centre, and gave half to the important personage, and retained half himself. As he did so, he said, "Whilst fishes have scales, and birds have feathers, I will do all I can for you, and so will every other man who belongs to the Brotherhood of the Grey Goose Feathers."

Well, the King's advisers seemed quite satisfied to let Porter take him across the Fens alone. When they arrived at St. Ives, they had to cross the river by a ford. Guarding this ford was two of Cromwell's soldiers. But when Porter produced the grey feather, they said, "Pass, all is well." They were Fenmen. So eventually King Charles arrived at the Bell Tavern, in Huntingdon, and he gave a reward to Porter for taking of him over, but he retained the grey goose feather. Some time afterwards, the king was taken prisoner, but before that happened, one of the officers in charge of the troops in Cromwell's army heard about how the sentry let them through, and he brought them along to Cromwell. But Cromwell was a Fenman too; so he said to that officer, "It is better for a king to escape than for the Fenmen to go back on a man who carries the split goosefeather."

So he let the men go, and not long after that King Charles was caught, and they brought him up to London and tried him, and he was sentenced to death. But the night before the execution, when Cromwell was sitting down to supper with his staff, a messenger came from the king, and Cromwell told his servant to let him in.

The messenger said: "His Majesty does not beg for mercy, but he demands as a right the help you must give to every man who carries this token."

And he flung down a grey goose quill on the table in front of Cromwell. Cromwell told everyone to go out, and he sat looking at the grey goose feather. And in the morning when the servants came in he was still looking at it.

Well, the king was beheaded, but Cromwell was never the same man again. He brooded and brooded, and what made things worse, all the Fenmen, who had served him well up to that time, sent back their goosefeathers, all broken and bent, and they said they were going back to the Fens, where there were still men who kept their word. And as he'd been false to the old custom of the feather, none of the promises that went with it would ever be made to him or any of his family again.

• 40 • *Swayne's Leaps*

Recorded from Ruth L. Tongue, September 29, 1963, as she heard the account from a laboring man in the Polden Hills, Somerset, in 1947. She heard other versions at Knowle St. Giles, two miles outside Chard, in 1959; in Eddington, 1962; and in Saltonstawell in May, 1963. Stones (since moved) were placed to mark the leaps in Loxley Wood.

Discernible motifs are F1071, "Prodigious jump"; F1088, "Extraordinary escapes"; and K551.28, "Captors give captive respite in order to witness alleged marvel."

• THIS HERE Tom Swayne he weren't much of a chap to have around a farm, but he could jump wonderful and he was surprising fond of his dear wife and little ones. Now there was a lad, out over, could run so fast as his father's hoss, and there was to be a match between the pair, see—who was champion. Then "the war" come—down over there on the moors, and Tom Swayne and this young chap they was both took. Well, they cruel devils did promise the young chap he was to be spared if he can match with a bay colt and win, which he did. Then they devils hang him high with other honest men! Oh 'twas a time of tears and sadness, 'twas. Now, Tom Swayne he's in a turrible fright in case he do swing then and there, but they marches him along this here road to Street. Well, his dear wife and the children run out to beg and pray for his life and his heart do nearly break in two.

Then he say to they soldiers, "Looky zee, have 'ee ever heard tell of a man as could jump from where we do stand now right to the edge of thic wood in dree leaps?" They wouldn't have it, but he say, "Let's have a try and you can bet on it. I'd a-wish my little children to remember my powers."

Now, a Moorlynch man would ha' been looking out for a bit of a trick, but they sojers didn't know he. They loosed his bonds and he do leap. One: fifteen feet. Then he do leap. Two: eighteen feet. Then he do leap. Dree: twenty-one feet—right over edge of wood and down in under the fern—and they'd a-lost their prisoner. When all them days was gone by Tom Swayne he come home to his own dear souls all safe and sound.

·41· *The Lost Bride*

Recorded from Ruth L. Tongue, September 21, 1963, who heard the story from "Annie's Granny" in her old age when she was in an almshouse at Chard or Yeovil, in Somerset, about 1920.

This version is about Shapwick, where a stone in the chancel of the church tells of the "daughter and heiress of the family honor and estates who died June 14, 1681. Taken away by a sudden and untimely fate at the very time of the marriage celebrations."

There seems to be no European counterpart to this story, which is not given a number in the Motif-Index. There are several versions of it in England, all supposed to be historical, though with very little foundation. It is also well known in the United States, mainly by reason of Thomas Haynes Bayley's Song, "The Mistletoe Bough," which was a popular item in village concerts, and which became traditional in the United States, though with very little variation either in words or tune. See Maurice W. Disher, Victorian Song: from Dive to Drawing Room *(London, 1955), p. 89. The explanation attached to the song has undergone more folk mutation, for the bride is usually described as a princess. In England the song is generally supposed to relate to a bride of the Yorkshire Lovels of Skelton, but Minster Lovel in Oxfordshire also claims to be the scene of the tragedy, and Broomshill in Hampshire is another claimant.*

• 'TIS A TURBLE zad tale, zo tis, but it do go thisaway. Parson had a darter, a purty young thing her was, and her was agettin' wed to her true love. There was a fine junketings and there they all was playing old games and merriment. And her went to hidey in a girt big chest, in attic 'twas, and lid come down crackey on poor maid's head and her fell in a swound inzide chest, and chest did lock itself. They did go lookin' up and down for the bride and no one could find she—and her true love's heart did break zo they buried the poor young man—but her never come back no more. Nobody could tell where her was to; then one day they come into the attic for something or another and opened the chest—and there her lay in her wedding gown, and her were just a skeleton.

•42• *The Thievish Sexton*

Recorded by Ruth L. Tongue, September 29, 1963, who heard her version in Watchet, in Somerset. The legend is closely attached to St. Decuman's Church, Kentsford.

This is Type 990, The Seemingly Dead Revives, *and Motif*

K426, *"Apparently dead woman revives when thief tries to steal from her grave,"* reported in scattered instances throughout Europe, with 77 examples in the Irish Folklore Archives. Baughman cites five American and four English variants. E. S. Hartland reprinted two texts in Folk-Lore of Gloucestershire, County Folk-Lore, No. 1, Part 1 (London, 1892), "The Lady Restored to Life," pp. 27–28. In Yorkshire the heroine is a miller's wife; see Mrs. Gutch, Folk-Lore of the North Riding of Yorkshire, County Folk-Lore, No. 2 (London, 1901), pp. 386–88. A southern Illinois variant is reprinted in R. M. Dorson, Buying the Wind (Chicago, 1964), pp. 310–11. A German version was used in Zangerle's Puppet Theatre in Cologne. See Cyril W. Beaumont, Puppets and Puppetry (London, 1958), pp. 84–85, for the story outline and pictures of the marionette characters.

In no case has the story actually been substantiated, though there have often been cases of catalepsy recorded in the families concerned.

• YOUNG MISTRESS FLORENCE Wyndham, 'er were took ill, and in spite of all they could do for she, 'er died, and 'er dear 'usband, 'e were 'eartbroken. They took she from Kentsford Farm, where 'er lived, up to St. Decuman's Church, and they buried 'er in the family vault. And then, 'er poor 'usband were took back to Kentsford.

Well, that night, the sexton 'e came creeping back to church, and 'e opened the vault again. You see, she 'ad some lovely jewels, and e' 'ad a mind to they. 'E crep' in with a little lantern, and 'e took 'old of 'er cold 'and, and 'e wrenched off one ring and another, but there was one 'e couldn't move. So 'e took out 'is knife to cut off the vinger o' she, and it bled! Well, 'e were so terrified, 'e just stood there, quaking, and the vigger of the lady, all in 'er shroud, sat up. Well, 'e turned around, and 'e kick over the lantern, and there 'e stood in the dark, while something rustled past 'e and out. Well, 'e were that terrified, 'e come out o' the church, and 'e run, and 'e run, and 'e run. And in 'is terror, 'e run over the edge of Old Cleeve cliffs, and 'e dropped down ninety feet into the sea, and no one ever saw anything of 'im again.

Well, the volks down to Snailholt Farm, they found themselves awaked by a voice, and it were the voice o' Mistress Florence Wyndham! Oh! They shook and they shivered in their beds, and at last, young Missis, she says, "Well, Mistress Wyndham, she never did no 'arm to I. I'll go and see what ghost want."

So 'er took and 'er looked out o' chimmer window, and there were the young mistress alive, with 'er 'and bleeding. Oh! They took the poor soul in, put a cloak round she, and took 'er back to Kentridge, and what's more, 'er was alive and well for years arterwards, and give 'er 'usband two more lusty sons.

·43· Mr. Fox's Courtship

Recorded from Ruth L. Tongue, September 29, 1963, who heard this cante-fable (story with a song included) from a farmer's daughter who was told it by her grandfather in Thorn St. Margaret, Blackdown Hills, in Somerset.

Baughman assigns this a new subtype, 955C, Mr. Fox, and cites English variants from Yorkshire, Derbyshire, Cornwall, Gloucestershire, Buckinghamshire, Lincolnshire, and Cambridgeshire, and American ones from North Carolina, Tennessee, Missouri, Kentucky, and Indiana, all states with English and Scotch-Irish settlers. "The Oxford Student," told by J. O. Halliwell-Phillipps in Nursery Rhymes and Popular Tales *(London, 1849), p. 49, is an early version of this tale, but it has a close connection, too, with "Mr. Fox" as known by Shakespeare. The story nearest to "Mr. Fox" is "The Cellar of Blood," a gipsy tale summarized by T. W. Thompson in his manuscript notebooks (1914).*

Motif G661.1, "Ogre's secret overheard from tree" is present, and B651.1, "Marriage to fox in human form," is suggested.

The Robber Bridegroom *(Type 955, Grimm No. 40), widely spread throughout Europe, is much nearer to the "Mr. Fox" story; the riddle and the grave belong mainly to the English tradition.*

"Hose-bud" means rascal. Red-headed men are always mistrusted in Somerset.

FALSE FOXES

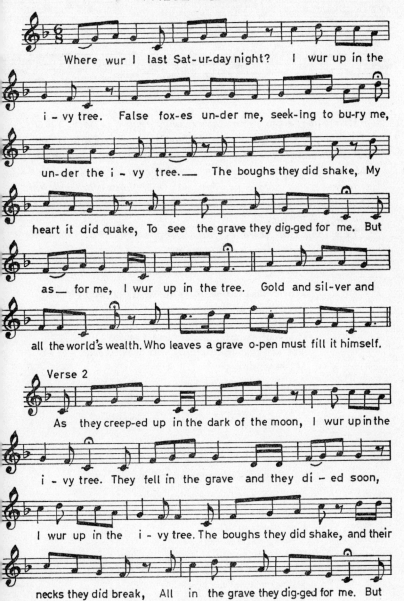

Where wur I last Sat-ur-day night? I wur up in the i - vy tree. False fox-es un-der me, seek-ing to bu-ry me, un-der the i - vy tree.____ The boughs they did shake, My heart it did quake, To see the grave they dig-ged for me. But as__ for me, I wur up in the tree. Gold and sil-ver and all the world's wealth. Who leaves a grave o-pen must fill it himself.

Verse 2

As they creep-ed up in the dark of the moon, I wur up in the i - vy tree. They fell in the grave and they di - ed soon, I wur up in the i - vy tree. The boughs they did shake, and their necks they did break, All in the grave they dig-ged for me. But

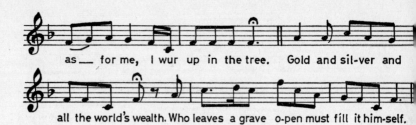

as ___ for me, I wur up in the tree. Gold and sil-ver and

all the world's wealth. Who leaves a grave o-pen must fill it him-self.

Miss Tongue knows two other songs upon this story. She also says, "A fragmentary version which seems to come from Somerset recollections was that of the maid who asked her suitor a riddle: ' 'Tis too little for a hoss, too large for a bee.' He couldn't answer her, so before her kinsman killed him she told him: 'Too little for a hoss, too large for a bee/I reckon 'twas the grave you digged for me.' "

This song was heard by Miss Tongue about 1910 and published in Word-Lore, *I (1926), p. 33.*

False Foxes (1)

Where was I last Saturday night? Up in the ivy-tree.
False foxes under me
Digging a hole to bury me.
One had a shovel, t'other had a spade
The one that had nothing was heaviest laid
My heart did ache,
And my tongue did shake
To see what a hole the fox did make
When I was up in the ivy-tree.

False Foxes (2)
From Blackdowns near Tipstable

Where were I last Saturday night?
I were up in the ivy tree,
False foxes under me
Seeking to bury me
Under the ivy tree.
The boughs they did shake,
My heart it did quake
To see the grave they digged for me.

But as for me,
I were up in the tree.
Gold and silver and all the world's wealth;
Who leaves a grave open will fill it hisself.

As they creeped oop in the dark o' the moon
I were up in the ivy tree.
They fell in the grave and they di-ed soon;
I were up in the ivy tree.
The boughs they did shake, their necks they did break,
All in the grave they digged for me.
But as for me
I were up in the tree.
Gold and silver and all the world's wealth;
Who leaves a grave open will fill it hisself.

• THERE WERE A young maid as had a girt vortune in gold an' silver an' a red-headed hose-bud called Mr. Fox came a-courting she. He'd a tongue on him zo smooth as scald cream and the maid her liked 'n more'n a bit. But she didn't trust'n mind, not altogether, so when he ask her to meet'n over-right the covert one Saturday night her didn't gainsay'n nor yet her didn't zay no. Mind he were sure she'd go and she was bound to zee for herself zince her mind wasn't quite clear 'bout 'n.

Her bedecked herzelf and 'er went there early on and was up top of a girt tree when Mr. Fox comed by. And he didn't come alone nuther! There was the two of en a-digging a grave right under the tree. Then they took out knives, so they did, and they waited for the maid to come along, see. Well, they waited and they waited. Her zoul a'most vailed her and she was ready to swound to find he wasn't worth a nort. But her were a spirity maid! And when morning come she did climb down and go on home. The next time Mr. Fox come a-courting and showing all his teeth properly agrin, she asks'n a riddle, see.

Last Zaturday night as I zat high,
Awaiting vor one but tew come by,
Tree it did bend, my zoul it did quake
Vor to see the hole they two did make.

Then Mr. Fox he stops agrinning all to a sudden and he outs the window like a vlash of vire. But the maid her'd a-told the Hunt where he was to and there they all was a-waiting vor'n. Don't reckon he digged no more graves for pretty young maidens with vortunes.

•44• *Drake's Cannon Ball*

Recorded from Ruth L. Tongue, September 28, 1963, as she heard the legend from a member of Watchet Women's Institute in 1950, and in Chipstable, on the Devon border, in 1960.

Sir Francis Drake was believed to be a magician by the Spaniards, but his reputation was no better among his fellow Westcountrymen. Various stories of his magical feats are told by Mrs. Bray, The Borders of the Tamar and the Tavy, *Vol. II, pp. 28–34; and Robert Hunt,* Popular Romances of the West of England, *First Series (London, 1865), "Sir Francis Drake and His Demon," pp. 260–62; and repeated by Christina Hole,* English Folk-Lore *(London, 1940), pp. 146–67. The people around Combe Sydenham still believe that Drake's cannon ball rolls up and down in times of national danger, and his drum was said to sound during the Second World War. John Henry Newbolt's poem, "Drake's Drum," commemorates this belief* (Collected Poems 1897–1907, London, 1910, pp. 15–17).

Motifs present are H335.4, "Suitor task: to defeat enemies"; D1123, "Magic ship"; and, in Baughman, G295*(g), "Wizard produces gunboats from pieces of wood in water" and G295*(k), "Wizard throws cannon ball several thousand feet to prevent second marriage of wife who thought him dead."

• THERE WERE ONE o' the Sydenham maids, and 'er got 'erself betrothed to Sir Francis Drake. But afore they could be married, 'e 'ad to go away on a voyage, and 'ow long it'd be afore 'e could come back, no one knew, and 'e didn't trust 'er father. So they took their troth-plight, the two of 'en, afore Drake sailed away. Well, 'e sailed away, for three long years, and Sir George

Sydenham, 'e found another suitor for 'is daughter, a much richer one. Well, no matter what the maid do say, marriage were announced, and she were half afraid o' Sir Francis Drake, but she were more afraid of 'er father. So she give in.

Well now, Sir Francis Drake, 'e did do some very strange things—'e did sit on Plymouth 'oe, a-whittling of a stick, and all the chips that fell into the sea, they did turn into ships, to go fight the Spanish Armada. Now, although 'e'd been gone three years, 'e knew what was 'appening, so at the very door o' the church, 'e dropped a red-'ot cannon ball in front o' the bridal party. Oh! give 'en a fright, did—and when 'e come 'ome at last, 'twas to find 'is bride and 'er dear father a-waiting for 'en with smiles. As for t'other bridegroom, 'e'd a-taken 'isself across the length and breadth of England. But I expect Sir Francis Drake knew where 'e was tew!

• 45 •   *Marshall's Elm*

Recorded from Ruth L. Tongue, September 28, 1963, as she heard the account in 1946 on a riding tour in Somerset from a Glastonbury farmer. She had heard previous mentions in the early 1920's from friends in Street.

This tradition is one of the many instances of the deeply rooted memories left in Sussex by the experiences of the Monmouth Rebellion in 1685, when James Scott, Duke of Monmouth, rebelled against James II, claiming he was the legitimate son of Charles II.

Applicable is Baughman's Motif G271.4.1(a), "Exorcism by burning or boiling animal heart stuck with pins (commonly nine). Usually this process brings the witch to the scene because of the burning it sets up in her heart." For a cow or bullock's heart he gives fourteen references from northern to southern England.

For discussions of the "Bloody Judge" Jeffreys see John Tutchin, The Bloody Assizes, ed. J. J. Muddiman (Edinburgh,

9

1929), and Hilaire Belloc, James the Second (*London, 1928*),
pp. 187–91.

*"Marshall's Elm" is the name of the tree on which the boy
was hanged; it was still standing in 1946. "Urchin" is a
hedgehog.*

• THERE WERE A varmer o' Walton near Street. 'E 'ad a only son,
and 'e were tremenjus proud of 'e. Well, the lad, like so many
more lads, 'e went to fight for Duke o' Monmouth down to
Sedgemoor battle, and 'e were taken a prisoner. Well, 'is vather
'e were frantic, and 'e try and 'e try to get the lad's life saved. 'E
spent all 'is savings, and 'e sold 'is 'arvest, and 'e took 'en to Judge
Jefferies. And then, 'aving took all 'e 'ad to offer, the Bloody
Judge gave orders the lad should be 'anged right afore 'is 'ome.
Well, they did so, and the vather 'e stood by, and when 'twas all
over, 'e turned round wi'out a word, and 'e go down to stables,
and 'e kill 'is best bullock. And then 'e pull out the girt 'ot
bleeding 'eart o' 'im, and 'e drove nail arter nail through 'en, till
it looked like a red urchin. Then not saying a word, 'e go back
to kitchen, and 'e carry the 'eart there, and 'e nail it up in the
chimney, where 'twas smoked and scorched for years.

And arter that day, the Bloody Judge, 'e were taken wi' chok-
ing coughs, and scorching burning pains all round 'is 'eart,
which pierced 'en right through. And whenever 'e got an attack
like that, there come a sight afore 'is eyes, no matter whether 'e
closed 'em or no—the sight of a 'anging lad.

• 46 • *Jack White's Gibbet*

*Recorded from Ruth L. Tongue, September 9, 1963. This ver-
sion was heard in a composite discussion at Wincanton in 1948,
but Miss Tongue had been familiar with the story from 1906
onwards. A very popular Barnstormers play on the subject is still
performed in Somerset.*

*An article on the actual event and the traditional accretions
of the story was contributed by H. B. Irving to* The Somerset

Year Book *for 1922 (p. 60). The murdered man was killed
partly in a drunken quarrel and partly from motives of greed,
aroused ironically enough by a gilded Nuremberg token mistaken
for a guinea. The crime was easily proved, Jack White was
hanged and afterwards gibbeted on the scene of the crime. This
was in 1790. Popular imagination got to work, and not only was
the gibbet supposed to be haunted (Motif E274, "Gallows
ghost"), but the incident of the bleeding of the corpse in the
presence of the murderer (Motif D1318.5.2, reported by Baughman for Shropshire, Yorkshire, and Lincolnshire) began to be
told. A rumor that Jack White had unwittingly killed his own
brother even brought the tale into the orbit of the popular Tale-
Type 939 A, that of the returning son unwittingly killed by his
parents. (See No. 26, "The Son Murdered by his Parents," in
this volume.) This text is of particular interest to the folklorist as
an example of the way in which rumor and tradition work.*

• JACK WHITE WERE a ostler, 'e weren't a very good one neither—
a bit too fond o' cards 'e was; and 'e took to dipping 'is fingers
into other people's pockets to find the cash to pay back 'is debts.
Well now, there come a traveler to the inn, and 'e got over full o'
zider, and 'e wasn't very wise about things, and 'e let on that 'e'd
got a lot o' gold about 'en. Well, next morning, when 'e do leave
the inn, and go on 'is way, Jack White, 'e up and followed 'im,
and when 'e'd gotten up by the crossroads, 'e murdered 'im, dead.
Some say that 'e knifed 'im with 'is own knife, 'Twere a case-
knife, and the man were a sailor. Anyways, Jackie White, 'e took
the gold; and 'e run back to inn.

Well, someone came along, and they found that man all dead
and murdered in 'is gore, and they bring corpse down to town,
and they put 'en out, so's everyone should see 'en—see if they
recognise 'en; and the crowds did come from Wincanton and
Castle Carey, all round like, to see if they recognise dead man;
and Jack White, 'e just daresn't stay away. Well, when the
crowd began to press round like, to 'ave a look at the dead
corpse, Jack White, 'e got pushed to the front, and so soon as 'e
got pushed to the front, that there corpus's nose began to bleed,
a little bit, just a little trickle, but someone spied 'en, and they

said, " 'Tis a-bleeding! 'Ere!" And they looked round, and there were Jack White, so white as—oh! like a bit o' snow. And they pushed 'en a bit further near corpse and—well! blood came gushing out like, and they laid 'ands on Jack White, and they said, " 'Ere be murderer!"

And they took 'en, and they 'anged 'en, up by crossroads. And there 'e do 'aunt. Ah! They do say, some on 'em, as the man killed were 'is own dear brother, come 'ome from the seas, and Jack 'e never recognised 'e, and the brother never let on. And that's why Jack do 'aunt.

·47· *The Foreign Hotel*

Katharine M. Briggs heard this story from Agnes Hannam in 1915 in Yorkshire. Baughman has assigned it Motif Z552, "The mysterious disappearance. Guest mysteriously disappears from hotel room."

Alexander Woollcott attempted to trace the source of this legend in While Rome Burns (*New York, 1934*), *"The Vanishing Lady," pp. 87–94, but came to a dead end with a report in the* Detroit Free Press *in 1889.*

· A LADY AND her daughter were traveling abroad, and arrived late at night, very tired after an exhausting journey, at the hotel where they had booked their rooms. The mother was particularly worn out. They were put into adjoining rooms, and the daughter tumbled into bed and fell asleep at once. She slept long and heavily, and it was well on in the next day before she got up. She opened the door into her mother's room, and found it empty. And it was not the room into which they had gone the night before. The wallpaper was different, the furniture was different, the bed was made up. She rang, and got no answer to her bell; she dressed and went downstairs.

"Can you tell me where my mother is?" she said to the woman at the reception desk.

"Your mother, mademoiselle?"

"Yes, the lady who arrived with me last night."

"But, mademoiselle, you came alone."

"We booked in; the night porter will remember; we wrote for two rooms!"

"Mademoiselle indeed wrote for two rooms, but she arrived alone."

And wherever she asked among the servants she got the same answer, until she began to think that she must be mad.

At last she went back to England and told her friends what had happened and one of them went to investigate. He went to the consul and the police and at last he found out the truth. The mother had been more than tired when she arrived that night, she had been in the invasion stages of cholera. No sooner had she gone to bed than she was taken violently ill; the doctor was sent for, she died, and the hotel owners were filled with panic and decided to conceal all that had happened. The body was carried away, the furniture was taken out to be burnt, the wall was re-papered, and all the staff were told to allow nothing to be guessed of what had happened. They knew that not a guest would be left to them if it was known that cholera had been in the house.

·48· *The Stolen Corpse*

Recorded from Winifred E. Briggs, in Burford, Oxfordshire, November 3, 1963. She heard it in Canada from a cousin who had heard it in Leeds, Yorkshire. It is by way of becoming an international migratory legend. Stewart Sanderson of Leeds University is making a collection of various versions of the tale, some of them dating back twenty years. It is, however, traveling, for Laurits Bødker of Copenhagen had seen it as a newspaper story told about Poland, and Bengt Holbek, also of the Folkedigtning Institut in Copenhagen, knew it in September, 1963, having heard it from Gustav Henningsen—again about Spain— from a friend's friend. I have lately come across versions from Sussex and Kent. Richard M. Dorson heard an American variant in East Lansing, Michigan, December 31, 1963, localized in the Southwest.

· THIS STORY WAS told me by my cousin, who had heard it from a friend in Leeds, about a couple whom he knew, who went for a camping holiday in Spain with their car. They had taken his stepmother with them. She slept in a different tent to the others. On the morning that they struck, they were very busy, and they didn't hear anything of her for a while, and then, when they went to her tent, they found she had died, and rigor had already set in. They were in a great state, and they didn't know what to do, but they decided to roll her up in the tent, and put her on top of the car, and go to the nearest town, and go to the consul and the police. So they did this, and went to the town, and then they felt very cold and miserable, and they hadn't had a proper breakfast. So they thought they'd get a cup of coffee to revive them, before they went in search of the consul. So they parked the car, and went to a small cafe, and had their cup of coffee, and then came back to look for the car. But it wasn't there. It had gone.

So they went home to England without the car or the stepmother. But the difficulty was, they couldn't prove her will.

·49· *The Half-Cup of Tea*

Katharine M. Briggs heard this story from Mrs. Madeline Mills about 1915, in Perthshire. It suggests Motif H381, "Bride test: thrift," and Type 1451, The Thrifty Girl. See the Pennsylvania Dutch text in R. M. Dorson, Buying the Wind, pp. 146–48.

· THERE WAS ONCE a man who always complained that whenever he asked for a half-cup of tea he always got a full one. No woman, he said, could pour out a half-cup of tea; and if he met one who could he'd marry her because she'd be a wonder. Well, one day he went to a garden party, and a young lady whom he hadn't met before was helping his hostess.

She asked him if he'd like another cup of tea, and he said, "Just half, please."

She poured him out exactly half. He looked at her with great respect, and he thought she was a very pretty girl. He found out her name, and he saw a lot of her after that, and liked her more and more, and in the end he asked her to marry him. They were married, and on the honeymoon she said, "What made you first think of me?"

"Well, do you remember the first day we met?" said her husband, "when I asked you for half a cup of tea?"

"Oh, yes," she said, "I remember. There wasn't a drop more in the pot, and I was so ashamed."

· 50 ·   *The Five-Pound Note*

Katharine M. Briggs heard this anecdote from a friend from London, Percy Robertson, in 1912 in Perthshire. Baughman assigns it Motif N360 (a), on the basis of a newspaper story in the Indianapolis Sunday Star, *March 3, 1946, "The $50 Bill," written by Frederick W. Gillett,* This Week Magazine, *pp. 3-4.*

· AN ELDERLY BROTHER and sister lived together, and one day the sister wanted to go to town to do some shopping. So her brother gave her a five-pound note, and she set out. She traveled third class, and the only other passenger was a shabby old woman who sat opposite her and nodded. Miss M . . . . was sleepy too, after her early, hurried start, so she dozed a little too. Then she woke up, and thought it wasn't very safe to go to sleep in a railway carriage, alone with a stranger. She opened her bag to make some notes of what she had to buy, and the five-pound note wasn't there. She looked at her neighbor, who was sleeping heavily with a big old shabby bag beside her. Miss M . . . . bent forward and, very cautiously, she opened the bag. There was a new five-pound note on top of everything.

"Old scoundrel!" thought Miss M . . . . . Then she thought, "She's poor and old, and I oughtn't to have put temptation in her way." She wondered what she ought to do. It would cause a great deal of delay and bother to call the police, and it seemed cruel to get an old woman into trouble, but she must have her money. So, in the end, she quietly took the five pounds out of the bag, and shut it up again.

At the next stop, the old woman got out, and Miss M . . . . got to town and did her day's shopping, and came home loaded with parcels. Her brother met her at the station. "How did you manage?" he said, "I expected to find you up a gum tree. You left your five-pound note on the dressing-table."

Part III

Jocular Tales

·51· The Curious Cat

Recorded from Ruth L. Tongue, September 28, 1963, as she heard the story from a Hawkridge drover in Somerset in 1945.

This is another legend of Tarr Steps, a set of natural stepping-stones over the River Barle. Mouncey Castle is an earthwork near at hand. Two local sayings seem related to the story: When blame is imminent, "Give it back to the cat"; and when there is an unpleasant job to be done, "Well then, send the cat to have a look-see."

Type 1191, The Dog on the Bridge, embodies Motif S241.1, "Unwitting bargain with devil evaded by driving dog over bridge first." In the present text, the cat crosses on her own. Other familiar motifs are K210, "Devil cheated of his promised soul" and G303.9.1.1, "Devil as builder of bridge."

Conflicts and arguments between a parson and the devil are common in English folk tradition. An example is the repartee of the dauntless minister in William Henderson, Notes on the Folk-Lore of the Northern Counties of England and the Borders *(London, 1879), p. 278.*

· THERE WERE ONCE a curious cat over to Spire, a proper mischievous nuisance that cat were, always poking into anything new. He'd torment they pore liddle mice and birds shocking—just to see what they'd try to do. 'Twere a wonder he didn't get his whiskers scythed off in hay field and his tail broke to bits on dreshen-floor for he were always right in the way where nobody wanted 'n. But there, he'd bite and scratch and swear till every one wished him Somewhere Else.

One day he went for a walk and he found Mouncey Castle. "Now, who dropped this little lot?" say he. "I must go and see." Then in the woodside he come on a gurt stone, twelve foot or more, just dropped there, and he knew he were getting nearer. Then he heard yells of rage and off he scuttles to see what 'twas and it were the Devil and Parson, one on each side of the Barle and a new stone bridge atween 'n. "I'll have a look-see at that," says Cat and downhill he goes.

Says Parson to Devil, "You shan't have none of my souls be first step on your bridge. They bain't goin' Somewhere Else."

"You old black crow," yells Devil.

"If I be a crow," says Parson, "I bain't so black as yew!"

And just then puss walk out over onto Tarr Steps to look it over, no matter if he'd been invited or no. The Devil pounced on 'n like a lightning flash—and poor Cat goed Somewhere Else quicker than you could think!

•*52*• *The Last Man Hanged*

Recorded from Ruth L. Tongue, September 29, 1963. She was told the story by a farmer's daughter from Cannington near Bridgewater, in Somerset.

Walford was a tinker who committed a murder at the end of the eighteenth century. The gibbet from which his body was hung in irons was at a crossroads on the Quantock Hills; it is still known as Walford's Gibbet.

In an Irish myth a hanged man complains in the same way, but it is of being thirsty (Motif E422.0.1). The incident is elaborated in literary form by James Stephen, In the Land of Youth (London, 1924), Part I, "The Feast of Samhaim," pp. 3–128.

• ARTER WALFORD WERE 'anged up there to Dowsburgh, there was a lot o' talk down to the Castle o' Comfort Inn, and they got to talking, and then they got to drinking zider, and then one vellow getting a bit over-merry, they dared 'en to go up to Walford's Gibbet. Well, 'twere getting late at night, and being over full o' zider, 'e said 'e would, and off 'e goes. Well, no sooner be 'e out o' front door than a couple o' rascals gets out by back door, and straight up over the 'ill. Laughing to themselves, they come up through the barn, and the bushes like, till they come to the foot o' the gibbet, and they 'ided in bushes. And bye and bye they 'ears bootses coming up 'ill, getting a bit slower like, as they comes nearer to where gibbet was, and they chuckles to theirselves, and then boots comes a bit slower, like, and then out o' the air above 'em comes a voice—"Oh! Idn't it cold up 'ere! Be yew cold too?"

Well, by the time the yellow with the boots, and they two got down to Castle o' Comfort, they weren't cold no more.

·53· Dolly and the Duke

Recorded from Ruth L. Tongue, September 30, 1963, as she heard the tradition in the Polden Hills in Somerset from one of "Granfer's" family (name withheld by request) in 1904 and again in 1935.

Sedgemoor and the Bloody Assizes that followed it made a deep impression in Somerset. The battle of Sedgemoor was fought on the night of July 5, 1685, and, presumably, on that day Monmouth's ghost was seen. (See the notes to "Marshall's Elm," No. 45 in this book.)

Motifs present are E334.5, "Ghost of soldier haunts battle-field"; E585.4, "Revenant revisits earth yearly"; and E581.2, "Dead person rides horse."

"Urchin" is a hedgehog; "owl-light" is deep dusk.

· THERE WAS A farmer who had a farm by the Polden Hills, and Granfer 'e was a very old man, and 'is pony was also a very old pony. They reckoned she was nearly forty. And he and Dolly used to be sent off for the day, really to get him out of the way, and it would take him most of the morning to get Dolly harnessed up. She used to stand and go to sleep in the shafts while he pottered around. And then they'd send him to some village about a mile away. If it were two miles Granfer and Dolly would not be back all day. But otherwise she'd come daundering along the road, having a snatch of grass here, and a snatch of grass there, with Granfer sitting up in the seat fast asleep, and they would come back into the yard. No one worried about them, and when the farm was pressed for time, hay time, harvesting time, well, it didn't matter, Dolly would look after Granfer.

One July harvesting time, they were very busy. They got rid of Granfer and Dolly early in the morning. They reckoned he'd be back about six o'clock. Well, time went on, and they were still very busy out in field, and when it came to owl-light, neither Granfer nor Dolly had come back. Then later the moon rose— still they weren't back and suddenly somebody said, "Oh! Do 'ee mind what night 'tis? 'Tis the very night o' Sedgemoor fight, an' they say the ghost o' the Duke on a fine foaming black horse do go galloping along top road where Granfer be, and all who sees 'en faints from fear."

Well, the family got together, men and boys, and the women stayed at home and trembled, and they took lanterns and they took pitchforks, and then they took the family Bible, and off they went to see whether they could find the corpses of Granfer and Dolly. Well, when they got to the top, they could hear Granfer, e' was alive then. So somebody shouts out, "Granfer, be 'ee all right?"

"'Course I be all right," came an irate voice. Granfer was usually a most good-humored old man, but he was spluttering with rage.

So they came a bit nearer, and then one of the boys, being a bit incautious, said, "Granfer, did 'ee see the Duke?"

"Did I see the Duke then," splutters Granfer. "'E came galloping down the road on a fine black 'orse 'e did, right down the middle, an' the right o' the road was Dolly's! That didn't stop 'im. 'E come right on, and Dolly 'er took a look at 'im. One look, an' look what 'e done to my Dolly!" Well, the family looked, and the boys went away and hid themselves round a corner, so they could laugh. Granfer and the cart were on the slope of the verge on one side of a hedge, and Dolly, still in the shafts, was on the other. "Come right at us, 'e did," said Granfer furiously. "And there she went, took one look at 'e. She jumped the hedge, thought she was to Bridgewater Fair, an' at 'er age too, an' 'ow be us going to get 'er back?"

Well, they got her back, and her fat little behind was as full of prickles as an urchin. When they got home to the farm, of course there were a lot of questions. Then somebody again said, "Granfer, what were the black 'orse like?" "Oh! Too fine 'orse to be 'andled like that—the man weren't no 'orseman. Come leathering a good beast down the road like that! And look what 'e done to my Dolly!"

And to his dying day, Granfer would never hear a word about the Duke of Monmouth without snorting, "Man were no 'orseman. Didn't know 'is road usage!"

R. L. Tongue added:

"I knew the old man. He was a little round, apple-faced old man, rather like those you see in gardens now as dwarfs. He wore an old brown coat and leggings, and used to sit up there in the cart nodding in his sleep while the fat pony ambled along with him. And I know the bend in the road down which Dolly took the cart, when she jumped the hawthorn hedge."

·54· Summat Queer on Batch

Recorded from Ruth L. Tongue, September 27, 1963, who remembers this as a favorite story of an old North Somerset groom about 1907.

For Motif J1495.1, "Man runs from actual or supposed ghost," Baughman gives 11 American references, including Negro. Add Dorson, Negro Tales from Pine Bluff, Arkansas and Calvin, Michigan, p. 219.

A "batch" is a piece of open common land or moorland.

· THERE WERE A old widow body 'oo 'ad a little cottage up to Batch, and 'er come to market with 'er bits to sell, and she wouldn't go 'ome no how. Well, they axed 'en, and all she'd say was, "There's Summat Queer on Batch!" and not a word more. Well, Job Ash, 'e say to 'er, "Never 'ee mind, my dear, I'll go up Batch for 'ee. No fear." And 'e up and went.

'Twere a bit of a unket wind up to Batch, road was lonely,

and wind did blow whist. 'E got to cottage, 'twere a little cottage like, with a front door and back door opposite each other, and kitchen were one side o' passage, sitting-room were t'other side o' passage, and stairs was in cupboard. In 'e goes, front door were wide open, and 'e swing the bar acrost, and 'e go to back door, and 'e swing the bar acrost there. Then 'e take a look-see to sitting-room. Weren't no one there. Then e' gave a look-see to kitchen. No one there neither. Then 'e rub 'is 'ands together, and 'e think o' the drubbing they lads was going to 'ave.

'E opens door—cupboard door—upstairs to bedroom. When 'e got up to bedroom, wasn't no one there neither. "Where be they tew?" said Job and 'e come down, and front door were open— back door were open tew. Bar were set back. Well, Job 'e took a quick look-see outside back door, and it slammed tew be'ind 'im, and bar slid acrost. Well, Job, 'e took off round corner o' that 'ouse; 'e didn't stop to look—gets round by front door, as fast as 'e could, and just as 'e got to front door, that slam in 'is face tew, and bar come down acrost. Well, Job, 'e took a deep breath, 'e did, and then 'e takes a look over 'is shoulder, and there were Summat Queer standing right be'ind 'im. At that Job 'e took off down that road, like 'e were to Shepton Mallet races. 'E were a girt vleshly veller, and when 'e'd got about a mile or so, 'e sat down on a 'eap o' stoneses, and 'e puff like a pair o' bellowses, and 'e got out 'is neck-'ankercher, and 'e rub 'is face, thankful. And then 'e look down, and there's a girt vlat voot aside o' 'isn. Then 'e look up a little vurther, and there's a girt 'airy 'and by 'is knee. And then 'e look up a little bit vurther still, and there's a girt wide grin.

"That were a good race, weren't it?" sez it.

"Ar!" sez Job, "And when I've got my breath back, us'll 'ave another!"

·55· A Cure for a Witch

Recorded from W. H. Barrett, October 12, 1963, as one of his stock of traditions from the Cambridge Fens.

Witchcraft beliefs were very strong in the eastern counties of England, and indeed in most lonely districts. Salt has always been considered a prophylactic against witches, who were supposed to take no salt with their meat (G271.3, "Use of salt in exorcism of witch"). Even to ask for salt was enough to break up the witches' banquet. Witches habitually frequent churchyard graves (Motif D1278.1, "Magic churchyard mould").

Any joke against the parson was welcome to the Fenmen, who had a strong bias against all churchmen which dated back to the exactions of the monks of Ely (Motif X410, "Jokes on parsons").

• IN FENLAND A hundred years ago, the Fens was smothered with witches. Everybody believed in them, except the parson, and he had good cause to think there was something supernatural about them.

It happened like this. One night old Billy Bowers, the local poacher, was returning home with his bag heavy with what he'd found in the woods, and as he walked by the churchyard, he saw a flittering light. So he stopped on his way and peered through the fence, and saw that it was one of the so-called local witches gathering earth off a new-made grave. Well, Billy don't like to see that, so he went home, got his old muzzle loading gun, put a charge of gunpowder into it, and then filled it up with broken rock salt, which he used to use to cure rabbit skins. So he went back up the lane, and he saw this old girl's behind bobbing up and down in the lantern light. So he took aim, and he fired. Well, the screech the old girl gave woke everybody up in the neighborhood. They all opened their bedroom windows to hear her screaming. Soon they was congregating round the churchyard gate. One said, "This is a job for the parson." So he went along, called the parson up. The parson wanted to know what was the trouble. "Well," he said, "all the devils in Hell are running round the churchyard, shrieking their insides out."

So the parson got up, and he called this man in, and he said, "Before we go, we'd better have something to put some courage into us."

So he produced a bottle of whiskey, took a good drink himself, and then handed a good drink to the other chap, who, by the way, was the sexton. Then the parson put on his surplice, in case there was something, and he picked up one of these new-fangled oil lamps, grabbed a big stick, and went across to the churchyard gate. He wanted the sexton to go with him. The sexton said his was a day job, he wasn't paid for night work. No one else wanted to go. So the parson said he'd go on his own. As he went down the churchyard, the old girl who'd had a dose of rock salt in her buttocks saw something coming the other way. Her gave a scream, and run down the churchyard. The parson followed her. He caught his foot on a tombstone, the lamp flew out of his hand, and burst into flames. Billy thought it was time he took a hand. So he went into the church, and he rang the bells for all he was worth. That caused all the jackdaws in the church steeple to fly out, and hover just over the heads of the people standing in the road with lanterns. So Billy went along and wanted to know what they was all out there for at that time of night. Someone told him that the Devil was in the churchyard. He'd come out of Hell, and when he came out of Hell, there was a flame of fire went up into the sky, and they hadn't seen him [the parson] since, so they supposed the Devil had took him.

So Billy says, "Well, ain't none of you going in to see what's happened to him?"

They said, "No."

"Well," he said, "I'll go."

So he went along, and he found the parson laying there with his face all covered with blood, where he'd hit his nose on the tombstone as he fell. Billy said, "I'm surprised! That must have been a hell of a fight you was in. I wonder what the other chap looks like, you being so covered with blood."

But the parson said if he'd only help him home, he'd give him whatever he'd like to ask. So Billy helped him home, and the parson promised him that he'd have a brace of pheasants off of him all the time the game season lasted. But Billy used to sit in the pub, and tell his tale.

He said, "People as thinks they knows think there's a lot of ways of curing witches." He said, "There's only one—that is, pepper their hams with rock salt. That'll cure 'em!"

·56· *A Paddock in Heaven*

Heard by Katharine M. Briggs in Edinburgh in 1915 from D. Ellis, a teacher from Cornwall.

There exists a large modern cycle of stories about St. Peter and exclusive sects and individuals in Heaven. The Indiana University Folklore Archives has a folder labeled "Modern Jokes: St. Peter in Heaven" containing thirty-one comic stories on this theme. The central motif is X597*, "Jokes about new arrival in Heaven" (Baughman). A serious motif adapted to the joke is A661.0.1.2, "Saint Peter as porter of heaven."

· THERE WAS A man who had just died, and arrived in Heaven, and St. Peter was showing him round. Presently they came to a high wall. "Hush," said St. Peter. He fetched a ladder very quietly, and climbed up, beckoning the newcomer to follow him. They went stealthily up and peered over the wall. It was one of the Heavenly Meadows, and there were a lot of rather ordinary-looking people walking about in twos and threes.

"Who are they?" said the newcomer.

"Sh!" said St. Peter, "Don't let them hear you. They're the Primitive Methodists, and if they knew anyone else was in the place, they'd leave Heaven at once."

·57· *The Two Chaps who went to Heaven*

Printed by Edward M. Wilson, in "Some Humorous English Folk Tales, Part One," Folk-Lore, XLIX (1938), 190–91, No. 10, as told by Richard Harrison in September, 1937, who had heard the tale locally in Westmorland.

This is Type 1848, A Pebble for each Sin (Motif J2466.1), reported in only one or two instances from Ireland, England, France, Germany, and Belgium. Cf. R. M. Dorson, Buying the

Wind, pp. 80–81, "The Beans in the Quart Jar" (Maine). A related subtype is 1738C, "Chalk Marks on Heaven's Stairs," cited only from Finland. In the present text the gates of Heaven have taken the place of the earthly confessional.

• WELL, THERE WAS two chaps were going to Heaven; one was called Jack and the other one Joe. Jack started off up the ladder first, and Joe said he would wait at the bottom and see what happened; he hadn't the guts in him like Jack had. When Jack was nearing the top, he met St. Peter, and St. Peter asked him where he was going to, and how he directed (? he'd erected) the ladder to get as far.

Jack told him he was going on an expedition to Heaven, and his mate Joe was waiting at the bottom to see what happened, and if he didn't come back within two days, he would set off back home. St. Peter said, "I must have all your sins down on this slate before you can go any further."

It wasn't very long before Jack was trooping down again, and when he got to the bottom, Joe said to him, "What the hangment hesta co'e back for?" Jack said, "I've co'e back for a laid o' chalk; we've run out up yonder."

·58· *The Three Premiers who went to Heaven*

Printed by Edward M. Wilson, in "Some Humorous English Folk Tales, Part I," Folk-Lore, XLIX (1938), 191, No. 11, as told in December, 1937, by Richard Harrison of Crosthwaite, who heard it from a joiner in the neighboring parish. A variant of the preceding tale.

"Yam" means home.

• THERE WAS THREE premiers, an Englishman, a Scotchman, and a Welshman were going to Heaven. Well, they started off, and when they got to the gates, they saw the doorkeeper standing.

They took no notice of him for the minute, and he grabbed hold of the Englishman, and asked him where they were all going to. So they said, "Oh, we are going to Heaven."

So he said, "Well, I'll have to have your sins written down first, and for so many sins you'll have to canter once round the garden." And the garden was about fifty acres.

So the Englishman looked a bit surprised, the Welshman nearly fell, but the Scotty didn't much mind. When he'd weighed up all their sins, he said to the Englishman, "You have to run once round, so get along, and don't delay about it."

When he came puffing back, he told him to stand on the other side of the gates, and he told the Scotchman to run round five times.

When he landed back again, the doorkeeper said, "Where's t' Welshman at?" The chap standing by said, "Oh, he's just popped yam for his bicycle."

•59• *The Parsons' Meeting*

Printed by Edward M. Wilson, "Some Humorous English Folk Tales, Part III," Folk-Lore, LIV (1943), 259–60, No. 29. He collected the jest from Mrs. Joseph Haddow of Haycote Farm, near Bowland Bridge in Westmorland in September, 1940.

This is an element of Type 1738, The Dream: All Parsons in Hell (Motif X438) which, in the form of a recounted dream, is reported in northern and eastern Europe, and in French-Canadian and Negro traditions in North America. Baughman classifies the present text under Motif X459(d).

• IT WAS, LIKE, a parsons' meeting, and they were all sitting round t'fire, waiting of this one to come in. And when he arrived, he just looked round 'em all an' smiled. And t'main parson (what do you call him?) t'bishop, he just stood up an' asked him where he'd been.

"Wha!" he says, "I've been to Hell."

"And what was it like there?"

"Why, it was summat similar til it is here."
"And what's that?"
"Why, ye couldn't git round t'fire fer parsons."

·60· *The Churchyard*

Printed by Edward M. Wilson in "Some Humorous English Folk-Tales, Part III," Folk-Lore, LIV (1943), 260, No. 30. He collected it in September, 1940, from James Raven, a farm servant at Cawmire Hall, Crosthwaite, in Westmorland.

This is a fragmentary text of Type 1791, The Sexton Carries the Parson, and Motif X424, "The devil in the cemetery." An immensely popular tale (207 variants in Ireland, 131 in Finland). Baughman lists 4 references for England and over 30 for the United States. S. O. Addy in a Derbyshire version (Household Tales, pp. 4–5) cites a 1480 Latin text.

· THERE WAS TWO chaps coming home fra' work ya neet, an' one had left the other and he'd getten practically home, and he'd getten to t'churchyard. And he heard some voices over there saying, "Yan fer me, yan fer thee; yan fer me, yan fer thee." An' he got a bit frightened like, and he thowt it was t'divvil dishing t'dead out. So, when he plucked up courage, he went and had a look, and he found it was two lads that had robbed a orchard, dishing fruit out.

·61· *The Parson and the Parrot*

Printed by Edward M. Wilson in "Some Humorous English Folk Tales, Part II," Folk-Lore, XLIX (1938), 284, No. 24, as told him in August, 1937, by Richard Harrison in Westmorland. Wilson remembered hearing the tale as a schoolboy in Kendal during World War I.

This is a variant of Type 1833A, What Says David? (Motif

X435.1), *in which a member of the congregation replies literally
to the minister's question. Scattered instances are reported in
northern Europe. Baughman gives ten United States and four
other English variants (three from the Shakespeare jestbooks).
The popularity of talking-parrot comic stories is the subject of
an M.A. thesis by Neil Rosenberg, "An Annotated Collection
of Parrot Jokes" (Indiana University, June, 1964).*

• THERE WAS A captain who had a parrot, and he was going out
on a voyage, and he always took his parrot wherever he went.
When they'd got out to sea the ship struck an iceberg. All the
lifeboats had to be launched, and when everyone had got into
them the captain grabbed his parrot and put it into a bag, and
when the boat got to sailing, they came across another liner, and
half of them got into the boat, the captain and his parrot being
among them. When they were nearing land the captain let his
parrot out of the bag and it flew away into the town. It happened
to be Sunday morning, so it made its way into the church, and
got behind the vestry curtain. When the vicar got into the pulpit
the parrot flew out and settled right under his nose. And he told
the people to take no notice of it and he carried on with his
sermon. Then he said, "Now, my friends, what shall we do to
be saved?"

And the parrot said, "Pump, ye beggars, pump."

•62• *The Man that stole the Parson's Sheep*

Printed in S. O. Addy, Household Tales with Other Traditional
Remains, *No. 17, p. 18, as collected in Calver, in Derbyshire.*

This is Type 1735A, The Bribed Boy Sings the Wrong Song
*(Motif K1631), reported in scattered instances from Denmark,
Spain, Italy, Yugoslavia, and the West Indies. Baughman gives
five United States references.*

*"The Wee Boy and Minister Gray," collected by Hamish Hen-
derson from Jeannie Robertson and deposited in the Archives of*

*the School of Scottish Studies, is a racier version. The wee boy's
second song goes:*

> As I strolled out one Summer's day
> Who did I spy but Minister Gray?
> He was rolling Mollie amongst the hay,
> He was tossing her upside downwards.

A "may" is a maid.

• THERE WAS ONCE a man who used to steal a fat sheep every
Christmas. One Christmas he stole the parson's sheep, and his
son, a lad about twelve years old, went about the village singing:

> My father's stolen the parson's sheep,
> And a merry Christmas we shall keep,
> We shall have both pudding and meat,
> But you moant say nought about it.

Now it happened one day that the parson himself heard the
boy singing these words, so he said, "My lad, you sing very well;
will you come to church next Sunday evening, and sing it there?"

"I've no clothes to go in," said the boy. But the parson said,
"If you will come to church as I ask you, I will buy you clothes
to go in."

So the boy went to church the next Sunday evening, dressed
in the new clothes the parson had given him.

When the service was over, the parson said to the people,
"Stay, my brethren, I want you to hear what this boy has to sing.
It's gospel truth that he'll tell you." For he was hoping that the
boy would confess before all the people that his father had stolen
the sheep. But the boy got up and sang:

> As I was in the field one day,
> I saw the parson kiss a may;
> He gave me a shilling not to tell,
> And these new clothes do fit me well.

·63· The Two Little Scotch Boys

Printed by Edward M. Wilson in "Some Humorous English Folk Tales, Part I," Folk-Lore, XLIX (1938), 182–83, No. 2, as told him by Mrs. Joseph Haddow of Haycote Farm, near Bowland Bridge in Westmorland. She heard it from a traveling Scotchman some twelve years before.

This is a modern variant of a famous international tale, Type 922, The Shepherd Substituting for the Priest Answers the King's Questions. Related motifs are H691.1, "Riddle: How much does the moon weigh?" and H524.1, "What am I thinking?" Walter Anderson has written a celebrated monograph on the tale, Kaiser und Abt (Folklore Fellows Communications, No. 42, Helsinki, 1923). In the Grimms' Household Tales it is No. 152, "The Little Herdsboy," and in ballad form it is Child No. 45, "King John and the Bishop." Type 922 assumes a rabbinical hue in Folktales of Israel, a companion volume in this series, No. 38, pp. 94–97, "A Dispute in Sign Language."

Edwin C. Kirkland has discussed "The American Redaction of Tale Type 922" in Fabula, IV (1961), 248–59.

• THESE TWO LITTLE twins their parents was—one was Catholic and t'other was Protestant. When they got to school age both parents wanted them to go to their religion's school, like, so they said they wouldn't quarrel over it; one could go to one school and the other to the other. Both of these boys was good scholars, but one's master was jealous of him getting above his own son, so he said to him, "Before I put you top of your class, you've to answer me three questions, and I'll give you till to-morrow morning to answer them. First is, the weight of the moon, the depth of the sea, and what am I thinking about?"

When he got home he wouldn't play with his other brother who was sitting in a chair, so his brother asked him what was the matter. He said, "The master has given me three questions to answer before he'll let me be top of the class." His brother said, "What are the questions?"

When he told him, he said, "Never mind t'questions. I'll go to your school in t'morning, and you go to mine, and we'll ask our mates where one another sits."

So in the morning both brothers went to opposite schools, like. After t'master called his registers out he asked him to stand up and answer his questions.

"Now my first question is the weight of the moon?"

"A hundredweight, sir,"

"How do you make that out?"

"Four quarters in a hundredweight and four quarters in the moon."

He said, "Very good, my little boy. "Now," he said, "the depth of the sea?"

"A stone-throw, sir."

"How do you make that out?"

"When you throw a stone it'll go straight to the bottom."

"Very good, my little chap," he said; "the third and hardest question. What am I thinking about?"

"Please, sir, you're thinking I'm wee Bobby, but I'm not. I'm wee Tommy."

·64· *Father, I Think*

Printed by Edward M. Wilson in "Some Humorous English Folk Tales, Part I," Folk-Lore, XLIX (1938), 186, No. 5, with the comment, "Told by my father, Mr. Norman F. Wilson, in March, 1936, who heard it about sixty years ago, probably from a Kendal nurse-maid."

This is Type 1562, Think Thrice before you Speak (Motif J2516.1), sparsely reported from northern Europe. A Pennsylvania Dutch variant is reprinted in R. M. Dorson, Buying the Wind, p. 146.

· THERE WAS A boy who was always making silly remarks and

annoying his father very much. So one day his father said to
him, "Tommy, you are always making silly remarks without
thinking. Now, when you want to make a remark you must
always think three times before you speak."

The next day the father was standing with his back to the fire.
Tommy looked at him and then said very slowly:

"Father, I think—

"Father, I think—

"Father, I think your coat-tails are on fire."

"You silly boy! Why didn't you say so at once?"

·65· King Edward and the Salad

*Told to Katharine M. Briggs by Neils M. Lund, a Dane living
at Hampstead, in Perthshire in 1912.*

*A variant from the preceding tale, Type 1562, Think Thrice
before you Speak.*

· When King Edward VII was staying at Sandringham some of
his grandchildren were staying with him and were brought
down to lunch. The king had a guest to whom he was talking.
Presently, one of the little grandsons said:

"Grandpapa!"

The King went on talking.

"Grandpapa!"

"Be quiet, David."

"But, Grandpapa—"

"Little boys must be seen and not heard," said the King.
"Wait till I've finished talking."

He finished the conversation, and then said, "Well, what
was it?"

"Oh, it's nothing, Grandpapa. There was a slug on your
lettuce, but you've eaten it now."

•66•   The Rich Man's Two Sons

Printed by Edward M. Wilson in "Some Humorous English Folk Tales, Part Two," Folk-Lore, XLIX (1938), 284–85, No. 25, as told in March, 1936, by Richard Harrison who heard it from a farmer on Walney Island in Lancashire.

This is Type 1628*, So They Speak Latin, *reported only from Sweden.*

• THERE WAS A very rich man who had two sons. He'd had them schooled very well, and they were clever boys. He wanted them to go to India to learn foreign languages. He gave them plenty of money to go with, and hoped they would progress.

So they sailed on the boat, and when they got to India, one said, "Let's not bother about learning any foreign language. Let's have a right good time, and see a bit of the country." So they had parties and went about till a letter came one day saying that they had to come back again. So when they were coming on the boat, they were afraid what their father would say with not learning any language. So one said to the other, "Don't worry, we'll get out of it all right." When they got to England they hadn't very far to go home. They had two fields to cross, and one wall had some barbed wire across. So as they were thinking what to say, one of them spied a hen with all its feathers off its back. So he said, "I've got a fine word."

And the other said, "What is it?"

So he said, "Hen-scot-a-back-bo."

And his brother was quite delighted. So hurrying to get home to tell their father the word, the other tore his trousers with getting over the barbed wire.

So he said, "Ee! I've got a grand word!"

And his brother said, "What is it?"

So he said, "I-tory-en-to."

So when they got in, their father and mother gave them a hearty greeting, and told them they were going to have a party, and the boys had to give a demonstration of what they'd been learning. So when they got into the room, they had supper first and then their father told the guests what his boys were going to do. So one got up and said, "Hen-scot-a-back-bo."

And the other one stood up and said, "I-tory-en-to."

And their father said, "Well, I'll go to India an-shut-em-all."

·67· *The First Banana*

Heard by Katharine M. Briggs in 1944 while serving in the R.A.F. in Errol, Perthshire, probably from Mary Studholme of Cumberland.

Very soon after the beginning of the Second World War bananas became unobtainable in England, so that many children had never tasted them. Because of the blackout the trains were often not lit at night. It is against this background that the tale was told in England, but there are Wisconsin and Arkansas versions in which the actors are from the backwoods. See Baughman, Motif J2214(b), "Woman eats her first banana just before her train enters a tunnel."

· TWO LITTLE SISTERS were making a train journey alone, and opposite them was a soldier just come back from overseas, who opened his knapsack and took out two long yellow things.

"Like a banana?" he said.

"What is it?" said the eldest little girl.

"It's a banana; you take the skin off it and eat it; it tastes good."

The little girls looked at the bananas doubtfully, and then the eldest peeled hers and began to eat it. Just then the train went into a tunnel. The elder sister said to the younger, "Have you begun to eat your banana yet?"

"No," said the younger.

"Well, don't, because it makes you go blind."

·68· The Farmer and the "Parson"

Recorded from Ruth L. Tongue, September 28, 1963, who heard the rhozzum about 1907 from an old North Somerset groom.

This falls under the general motif X800, "Humor based on drunkenness." Also present is Motif F491.1, "Will-o'-the-Wisp leads people astray." A comparable anecdote is told in northern Michigan of a drunken lumberjack crawling along the main street of Sault Ste Marie. "Can I give you a lift?" asks a passerby. "You've got more than you can carry." "By God," he says, "if I can't carry her, I can drag her" (R. M. Dorson, Bloodstoppers and Bearwalkers, Cambridge, Mass., 1952, pp. 189–90).

"Rhines" are the deep ditches on the sides of roads. "Spunkies" are will-o'-the-wisps. "Four-wents" is a crossroads.

· THERE WERE AN old varmer coming whoame from Bridgwater Fair and he were proper market-merry. But he did try all ways to keep on causeway. There were a deep rhine to each zide of drove and he didn't want no cold dip. So he were extra careful. He knowed the road were straight as a withy till he comed to the four-wents, and he kept so near middle of it as any man could. But you wouldn' believe how that road try to trick him. It went up and down like a caterpillar, and he never knowed when to lift a foot high or put it down flat; then it would give a wiggle like and he'd find hisself with both feet set two inches above they cold deep rhines; and then to make things worse the spunkies come out all a-shining and a-beckoning all round he. They was all round the poor man, beckoning so it made him dizzy.

"I'll be at bottom of they rhines afore I can walk two-three steps," he say to hisself. "But I'll beat'n! I'll get whoame if I crawls." So he get down on his all fours and he go on up road which didn't zigzag near so much. He were quite proud he was making road behave at last, and beating they bothering spunkies, when he look up and there in the mist, right in front of him, were a girt white thing *and it had four arms!*

"Rhines and roads and spunkies!" groans varmer, "an' now 'tis ghosteses. I'll shut my eyes and go on." Well, he crawled and he crawled and every time he took a peep, there were thic terrible white thing above him. In the end he just lay down where he was, and slept, as clean wore out as the knees of his breeches.

When he woke up, sun was up, and he was flat on his face, below the parson at the four-wents.

"Why do you call it a 'parson'?" I asked.

"It do point the right way to go." (The general finish of this is "but it don't go there itself.")

·69· *The Irishman's Hat*

Printed by Edward M. Wilson in "Some Humorous English Folk Tales, Part I," Folk-Lore, XLIX (1938), 184–85, No. 3, as told in March, 1936, by Mrs. Joseph Haddow, who heard the tale from her father-in-law, who was a native of Ulverston.

A gipsy version is in the T. W. Thompson Notebooks at the University of Leeds, Vol. III, "The Hat that Paid," told by Gus Gray at Cleethorpe, October 7, 1914.

Motif K111.2, "Alleged bill-paying hat sold," appears as an element of Type 1539, Cleverness and Gullibility, known all over Europe, and in Asia and the New World. Baughman has provided a new subtype, 1539A, The Hat that Pays for Everything, citing a Texas reference besides the present text.

· THIS IRISHMAN, HE'D got fifteen pounds, and he didn't want to take it hay-timing with him, so he went to the first public house, and asked the landlord if he would keep five pounds for him. "Certainly." And he said, "When I come back I don't want everyone to know our business, so if I lift my hat and say, 'Do you remember the man with the white hat with the green band round it?', then you will give me the money." So he went to the next public house and said the same there, and to the third public house and said the same there.

And so when he was coming home from his hay-time place, a butcher with his cart overtook him. And they go on about money matters and the Irishman said, "I can get money when you can't." And the butcher said, "How will you manage that?" So they had a bet of five pounds. So when they came to the first public house, they went in and the butcher ordered drinks apiece. So when the landlord brought them, the Irishman lift' his hat, and said, "Do you remember the man with the white hat with the green band round it?" The landlord said, "Yes, there's five pounds for him"

So t'Irishman said t'butcher, "Come on, let's try t'next pub." And there they did all t'same again, and t'butcher called for drinks as before an' everything.

And they said, "Well, we'll go to t'next." And all was said again—he got his five pounds again, and so he got his fifteen pounds.

T'butcher said, "I think I'll try t'next."

And t'Irishman said, "You'll want this hat."

And t'butcher said, "How much for it?"

He says, "Five pounds."

So t'butcher, going into the next public house he came to, ordered himself a drink, and when landlord brought it, he lift' his hat and said, "Do you remember the man with the white hat with the green band round it?"

And t'landlord said, "No, what's up wi' him?"

He says, "Isn't there five pound for me?"

T'landlord said, "No, there's mi shoe if ye aren't gittin' out."

·70· *The Three Foreigners*

Printed by Edward M. Wilson in "Some Humorous English Folk Tales," Folk-Lore, XLIX (1938), 187, No. 6, from Richard Harrison of Crosthwaite, aged 16 in January, 1936, when he told this tale. He had heard it from a farm laborer born near Whitehaven.

This is Type 1697, We Three; For Money (Motif C495.2.2), known throughout Europe, and in India and the New World, Baughman lists New Jersey, Indiana, and Michigan Negro texts, the latter from Dorson, Negro Folktales in Michigan (Cambridge, Mass., 1956), pp. 183–85. A gipsy version is in the T. W. Thompson Notebooks, University of Leeds, Vol. VI, told by Reuben Gray, Old Radford, Nottingham, December 21, 1914. A Märchen form, Type 360, Bargain of the Three Brothers with the Devil, makes the replies the result of a contract with the Devil, who finally rescues the three from the gallows.

· THERE WAS THREE Frenchmen came to England and none of them could speak English. So to find out they went outside a public house and listened to see what they could hear. They heard one man say, "Us three." So the first man thought of that. Then they heard another man say, "Fifteen bob." So the second man kept that in his head. Then they heard a third man say, "Nowt but reet and should be done." So the third one thought of that.

The next day they saw a dead man lying in the roadside. And the policeman came on and said, "Who has done this?"

And the first man said, "Us three."

The policeman said, "What did you do it for?"

The second man said, "Fifteen bob."

And the policeman said, "Well, ye'll have to be hung for this."

The third man said, "Nowt but reet and should be done."

·71· *The Deaf Man and the Pig Trough*

Printed by Edward M. Wilson in "Some Humorous English Folk Tales, Part I," Folk-Lore, XLIX (1938), 187–88, No. 7, as told by Richard Harrison of Crosthwaite, who had heard the story five or six years before as a boy of eleven. It may be derived from part of a dialect piece, "Johnny Shippard at Heeam," written by the Rev. Thomas Clarke of Ormside, which sold widely in the past century.

Baughman adds to Type 1698B, Travelers Ask the Way *(Motif X111.2, "Deaf peasant: travelers ask the way"), the present Westmorland text and a similar one from the Carolinas. The Type-Index indicates four examples from India. Antti Aarne wrote a monograph on jokes about deaf people,* Schwänke über schwerhörige Menschen *(Finnish Folklore Fellows, No. 20, Hamina, 1914).*

• THERE WAS A man that was very deaf, and he was making a stone pig trough one day. And he saw a man coming along the road, and he knew he would ask him something about what he was doing. So he thought if the man asked what he was making he would say a pig trough; and if he said how much he wanted for it he would say fifteen shillings; and if he wouldn't buy it he would say, "If thou doesn't someone else will."

The man asked him the way to Bolton, and the deaf man said, "Pig trough."

And the man said, "I asked you if this was the way to Bolton."

And the deaf man replied, "Fifteen bob."

The other man said, "If tha's gaan to be cheeky I'll punch thi back-side."

And the deaf man said, "If thou doesn't someone else will."

•72• *The Borrowdale Cuckoo*

Printed by Edward M. Wilson in "Some Humorous English Folk Tales, Part III," Folk-Lore, *LIV (1943), 260–61, No. 32, as taken down in April, 1936, from James Harrison of Low Fell, Crosthwaite, who heard the tale in 1901 from a native of Thirlmere, Cumberland. Wilson comments that the tradition relates to Borrowdale, Cumberland; various printed versions exist, all derived from that recorded by J. Briggs in* The Lonsdale Magazine, *II (1821), 293. He feels however that the present text is genuinely oral.*

Type 1213, The Pent Cuckoo, *applies to this story, which Baughman reports (under Motif J1904.2.1) for Northumberland, Yorkshire, Shropshire, Nottingham, and Cornwall. John E. Field has devoted a full study to* The Myth of the Pent Cuckoo *(London, 1913). Outside of England only one Walloon variant is cited. This "noodle" tale is best known as part of the exploits of the Wise Men of Gotham, collected by Ruth Tongue in Somerset, 1913.*

"Intack" is enclosure; "shut (long ū) is to shoot; "steean" is stone.

• Now THEY WERE terribly bothered in Borradle about their game. There was summat ga'en on wi' t'game eggs, an' they couldn't reckon it up. Well, they was watching one day an' they spot t'cuckoo sowkin' eggs. They tried to shut it an' they couldn't git a shot at it, and so it flew into an intack, and intul a tree. And so they thought they would wa' it in. So they got a good wa' round it, but t'cuckoo cleered t'top—nobbut just. So they thought they was a steean or two short because it just cleered it.

So they went round where they had all this game an' t'cuckoo was there again. So they off wi' their guns again to see if they could shut it. Awwiver, it happened to flee and into just t'same intack, just an' so cleered t'wa'. And so they thowt they would put a bit mair wa' on top—they thowt they would have it. Awwiver, they went in again wi' their guns an' it flew out again, just an' so cleered t'wa' again. And that carried on for about fower times, and they wa'd up till they'd wa'd aw t'steeans there was in Borradle. So they had to give it up—it could allus flee ower just t'top.

•73• *Growing the Church*

Recorded from Ruth L. Tongue, September 28, 1963, who was told the story by L. Wyatt in 1913 in Somerset.

For Motif F802.1, "Big rocks grow from little rocks," Baughman cites examples from Herefordshire, Oxfordshire, Suffolk, and New York.

• THERE WERE A little village, and they were very proud of their church, 'cos in the next town there was another church, and they were as alike as two peas. Well, town people they went and they measured their church all round; and village people they measured their church all round, and they were both alike. And then they measured the spires, and town church were a little bit taller—only about a inch.

Well, village people were proper upset, they was. So they got together, and they 'ad a talk, and they were very busy that night, and when morning came, all the churchyard round little church were a girt 'eap o' muck, so's 'e'd grow 'igher.

•74• *The Jamming Pan*

Printed by Edward M. Wilson in "Some Humorous English Folk Tales, Part III," Folk-Lore, LIV (1943), 258–59, No. 26. Taken down in March, 1938, from Richard Harrison of Low Fell, Crosthwaite, in Westmorland.

Type 1351 (Motif J2511), The Silence Wager, *is distributed throughout Europe, with seven versions known in France, but it may be of Eastern origin since it is found in India, China, Iran, and Palestine. W. Norman Brown has studied "The Silence Wager Stories: their Origin and their Diffusion,"* American Journal of Philology, *XLII (1922), 289–317. In a Korean version, in Zöng In-Söb,* Folk Tales from Korea *(London, 1952), p. 191, No. 89, "A Selfish Husband," it is the husband who wins the contest. In* The Book of Noodles *(London, 1888), pp. 107–17, 181–85, W. A. Clouston presents examples from Kashmir, Ceylon, Arabia, Turkey, and Sicily. New World texts are known in Spanish, Portuguese, French-Canadian, and Negro traditions.*

English versions are hitherto unreported. Perhaps the liveliest form of the type is the Scottish ballad, "Get Up and Bar the Door" (Child No. 275).

"Drinking" here means elevenses. A "roadster" is a tramp.

• THERE WAS A farmhouse situated a long way from anywheres, about five or six miles from t'nearest house. At this farm they'd a terrible lot of fruit trees, and damson time had come round again, and they were short of a brass pan for jamming with. T'ald farmer says ya day, "Eh, lad, I want thee te ga down to ald Jack Sowerby's an' git their brass pan."

T'lad says, "Nay, hang it. I's nut ga-en fer a thing like that five mile. Neea nut I."

So he went til his wife and said, "Hey! Libby! thee slip down to ald mother Sowerby's an' ex her fer t'brass pan. Tell her we're gaan te jam."

"Nae damn fear!" she says, "I's nut gaan if jammin' nivver gits done!"

An' he says, "Ye stupid ald beggar, ye. What thee an' t'lad? It looks damn like I shall hev ta ga mysel." So he started off for it after they'd milked ya neet.

Efter aw t'jammin' had gitten done, it was time for t' pan te ga back again. But t'question was wha was gaan te tak it back? So they held a conference ya neet, an' it was gaan te fa' on t'ald farmer te tek it back hissel' again. So he says tul 'em aw ya neet, "Ah'll tell ye what ah'll dew; which yan o' us speaks after now this verra minute, hes t'pan te tek back," he says, "I's damn sure it'll nut be me." Then the silence began.

The family went to bed, nobody saying owt. Next mornin' they aw gat up—still t' tongues was quiet. Aw went like that till drinking time. Then there was a girt rattle on t'dooer. Neeabody answered it. So this here chap walked in—he was a girt big roadster—a bad lookin' sort of a chap he was—he says, "Good mornin'—grand mornin'." Still silence, so he collared a girt lump o' pastry and hed a pint o' tea. Aw was still silent, so he crammed his belly as full as he could git it. He had a peep in one o' t' drawers, spot' a ten bob note, and pocket' it. Still silence among the others. So he walks up to t'ald woman. "By gum," he says, "ye're a smart lookin' woman. D'ye mind if I gi'e ye a kiss?" Still silence, so he gev her yan.

Then he walks up to t'dowter, he says, "By gum! thou's as good a lookin' as thi mother. Dosta mind if I gi'e ye yan?" He was a little bit capped that nothin' was said after all he'd done. So he gave her a kiss.

Then he turned to t'ald lad, "Na, come on. It's thy turn now!"

T'ald farmer said, "Nay, damn it. I'll tak t'pan back."

•75• *The Contrary Wife*

Printed by Edward M. Wilson in "Some Humorous English Folk Tales, Part I," Folk-Lore, XLIX (1938), 183–84, No. 2, as told in 1936 by Mrs. Joseph Haddow, who heard the story from a neighboring farmer, who heard it from an old woman in Ambleside, in Westmorland.

Type 1365A, Wife Falls into a Stream *and Motif T255.2, "The obstinate wife sought for upstream" are most heavily reported in Finland and Sweden. They are attached to the Balkan character Hodja Nasreddin; see Henry D. Barnham, trans. (from the Turkish),* The Khoja: Tales of Nasr-ed-Din *(New York, 1924), p. 191, "The Khoja's Mother-in-Law Drowned." Baughman lists two English and two North American examples.*

"Yam" means home; "leeat" is late; "tull" is to; "seeaf" is safe; "hafe" is half; "back" is stream.

• THIS FARMER WAS brought up for murder of his wife. Well, after t'judge had been talking all afternoon to him t'farmer said, "It's about time ah was ga-en yam to feed. But before ah go ye'll like to kna how it ah happened."

And t' judge said, "That's what we've been asking you all afternoon."

"Well," t'farmer said, "it was this way. My wife was one of them contrairy soort. An' gittin' up late one Sunday mornin' ah said, 'We'll nut ga to t'church this mornin'; it's gitten a bit leeat.'"

"And she said, 'Yes, we will. Git thysel finished and we'll gang.'"

"So when we set off ah said, 'Shall we ga t'nearest way?'"

"And she said, 'No, we'll ga this t'other way.'"

"So ga-en the way as she wanted us tull, we 'ad to ga across a wooden brig, an' ah says tull 'er, 'Ah'll ga t'first an' see if it's seeaf.'"

"She said, 'Nay, ye wain't; I's gaen t'first.'"

"And when she got hafe-way across, t'brig ga'e way, an' she went in. And me thinking she would be still contrairy, ah ran as 'ard as ah could up t'beck. An' she was that jolly contrairy she went t'udder way. And so when ah got er oot, she was deead. She's been contrairy aw er life," he said.

·76· *Knife or Scissors*

Printed by Edward M. Wilson in "Some Humorous English Folk Tales, Part III," Folk-Lore, LIV (1943), 259, No. 27, as taken down in January, 1938, from Mrs. J. E. Bland, a native of Hull, now resident at Endmoor in Westmorland. She heard the story in Hull as a little girl.

Type 1365B, Cutting with the Knife or the Scissors (Motif T255.1, "The obstinate wife: cutting with the knife or scissors") is reported in forty-four examples from Sweden, with scattered instances throughout Europe. Baughman gives references from six American states, as well as from Alberta, Canada, and from Westmorland (the present text), and Norfolk in England. A recent text from Maine is in Dorson, Buying the Wind, *p. 84.*

• THERE WAS A man and his wife having an argument about something that had been cut. The man said it had been done with a knife, and the wife said, No, it had been done with scissors. And they kept on arguing till they got so angry with each other that he pushed her into the pond. And he kept on shouting "Knives" from the bank, and she kept shouting "Scissors" from the water, as long as she could shout; each was determined to have the last word. And at last he called "Knives" and he was quite pleased with himself because he thought he'd won; she didn't call back.

But much to his disgust—he thought he'd have a last look at

her—and as she was sinking she was there [here my informant paused and made a cross with her two forefingers] with her fingers crossed.

·77· *The Farmer and His Wife and the Mirror*

Printed by Edward M. Wilson in "Some Humorous English Folk Tales, Part III," Folk-Lore, XLIX (1938), 277–78, No. 14, as heard from Richard Harrison in March 1936, who heard the tale from a native of Cartmel Fell, in Westmorland.

Type 1336A, Man does not Recognize his own Reflection in the Water (Mirror), and Motif J1795.2*, "Man finds mirror, thinks it is a picture of his grandfather" (Baughman) are irregularly distributed in eastern Europe, Asia, Hawaii, and the United States in scattered examples. Baughman cites a New Mexico and a Missouri text. A recent Maine text is given by Dorson, Buying the Wind, pp. 81–82. In its complete form—a third person looks into the mirror—it is commonest in Japan, with fifteen variants reported. One of the best is "The Nun as Judge," in Keigo Seki, Folktales of Japan (a companion volume in this series), No. 55, pp. 188–89, where a nun arbitrates between husband and wife. Interestingly, the story was printed in Arthur Mee's The Children's Encyclopedia, 8 vols. (London, 1908–10), as a Japanese tale.

· ONCE THERE WAS a farmer who had a lot of land, and he looked well after his land, and kept everything in the best order he could. And one Sunday there'd been a lot of picnickers in one field and they'd left a terrible lot of litter. So the next morning after he'd finished his work, he would go and pick it up. And he searched about amongst it and he found a looking glass, and he said: "Ee! My! That's just like mi grandfather and mi girt-grandfather," he said, "I wonder where they've gitten that photograph at." He said, "I'm takin' that yam, and I'll treasure it an' aw."

And when he got home he started off upstairs to put it in a

drawer. And his wife wondered what on earth he'd gone upstairs for so early in the day. So she thought she'd watch him and see what he was doing. She saw him put something into the drawer, so she thought when he'd come down she'd go up and have a look.

So after her husband came down she went upstairs and very quietly opened the drawer. And she picked out this looking glass, which she thought was a photograph. She held it up and said, "That's the bloomin' old geyser he's been knocking about wi', is it?"

·78· The Three Obedient Husbands

Printed by Edward M. Wilson, "Some Humorous English Folk Tales, Part II," Folk-Lore, XLIV (1938), 282–83, No. 21, as told to him in April, 1937, by Richard Harrison of Crosthwaite, then 17, who heard the tale from a fisherman on Walney Island, in Lancashire.

This tale is given Motif N13, "Husbands wager that they will be able to do what wives tell them," but so far it is unique.

"Ta-morn" is tomorrow; "play pop-weasel" and "play shell" mean to grow angry and scold; "lile" is little.

· THERE WERE THREE chaps in a public house, and when it came to closing time they went outside and one of them said, "I've gitten an idea, chaps. Which yan o' us doesn't do as t'wife tells us ta-neet when we ga yam es ta pay for drinks round ta-morn t'neet."

They all agreed to it, and they all met as usual t'next neet, and t'first chap started off and he said, "I gat yam an' she started playing pop weasel. So I thowt, if she could mek such a row I could 'elp it on, so I started. An' then she said, 'Aye, that's it. Ga an' wakken aw t'street up.' So I did dew. So I's clear. I'll ev a smook and hear you other chaps now."

T'second fellow said, "I think I'll clear mesel'. I gat into t'house; I allus hev a drink o' milk afoor I ga to bed, an' as I was fillin' mi pot a lile drop spilt o' t'flooer. An' she said, 'Aye, throw it all ower t'flooer.' So up wi' t'jug an' I did dew. So I's clear aw rcct."

T'third fella, scrattin' his head, said, "I was sure it wad be me. I gat into t'house and she met me at t'dooer wi' t'poker. And just as I gat sat down she let go wi' it, an' just grazed me heead. And t'usual thing, she started playing shell; shoutin' she did was turble. An' I was as bad. An' then she said, 'Oh! ga an' drown yersel.'" And he said, "Eh! I hadn't the heart to dew it."

•79• *The Lazy Wife*

Recorded from Frank Rose, Swinbrook, Oxfordshire, on August 12, 1963.

Motif W111.3 is "The Lazy Wife." A variant of the present jest, collected from a Cornishman in Michigan, is in R. M. Dorson, "Dialect Stories of the Upper Peninsula," Journal of American Folklore, LXI (1948), 137, No. 37, "Fire! Fire!" The responsibility of the country wife for seeing that the fire stayed lit all night and was revived in the morning is discussed by E. Estyn Evans in Irish Folk-Ways (London, 1957), p. 71.

• THERE WERE A farmer 'as had a very lazy wife. Long ago when they used to keep 'orses on the farm and they 'ad the old carters, they used to go out early to feed the 'orses and come back to breakfast. So when they got back the wife was still in bed. So 'e went to the foot of the stair and he shouted, "Fire! Fire! FIRE!"

Then she come rushing down in 'er nightdress, and say, "Where 'er?"

"Everybody's 'ouse but ours," 'e says.

•80• *The Lad Who Was Never Hungry*

Printed by Edward M. Wilson, "Some Humorous English Folk Tales, Part I," Folk-Lore, XLIX (1938), 185–86, No. 4, as told in September, 1937, by Mrs. Emily Harrison, a native of Askam-in-Furness, who since her marriage has lived in Crosthwaite. She heard the tale when she was hired at Ulverston Fair from an old farmer who came from Preston. The tradition then belongs to Lancashire. The farmer tells it on himself.

Type 1561, The Lazy Boy Eats Breakfast, Dinner, and Supper One after the Other is scattered throughout Europe. Baughman lists variants from Kentucky, Wisconsin, and Indiana. The latter text, from the Bloomington area (The Federal Writers' Project in Indiana, Hoosier Tall Stories, 1937, p. 13, "Mighty Good Policy") is closest to the present form. A Mexican-American text from New Mexico is reprinted in R. M. Dorson, Buying the Wind, pp. 447–48.

· THE FARMER was talking to the lad at the hiring fair.

T' farmer asked him if he was a good getter up.

"Oh, aye," he said, he was a good getter up, he says, "ye kna ah's nivver tired, ah's nivver hungry, an' ah's nivver dry."

"Oh!" he says, "Tha's just t'reet fella for me."

So when he lands up to t'place, whatever's set before him he eats it, whatever he has to drink he drinks it all, and whenever he went to bed he always went in good time—nine o'clock prompt. So it went on for a few days, so t'boss said to him, "I thowt thou was nivver hungry, nivver dry, an' nivver tired."

"Nay," he said "it's o' this way. I it afoor I's hungry, I sup before I's dry, and ah ga to bed afoor I's tired."

·*81·* *Take a Pinch of Salt With It*

Recorded from Ruth L. Tongue, September 28, 1963, who heard the incident at Langport Women's Institute in 1960. Langport is above the flat moorland of Sedgemoor, in Somerset.

An Aberdeen version is told as a campfire yarn by Helen Duff, Black Islands.

· THERE WERE A varm lad, and 'e went out on a job, and someone met 'e down to Langport town, and said to 'im, "Tom, what be doing 'ere? I thought 'ee 'ad a job down over."

"Ah," 'e said, "I did, but first one o' they sheep died, and us put un down to zalt, and us lived on that; then old cow died, and us put un down to zalt, and us lived on that. And last week, the Missus died, so I comed on 'ome."

·82· Old Charley Creed

Recorded from Ruth L. Tongue, September 28, 1963, who heard the story from Mrs. H .... in Crowcombe Women's Institute, in Somerset.

Cf. the variant of Type 1738, The Dream: All Parsons in Hell, printed as No. 59 in this book, "The Parsons' Meeting." Two texts similar to the present one about dreams of favored persons in Hell, from Maine and Massachusetts, are summarized from printed sources in R. M. Dorson, Jonathan Draws the Long Bow (Cambridge, Mass., 1946), pp. 56–57. See Baughman, Motifs X459(e) and X688*(a).

• YOU REMEMBER OLD Charley Creed, lived down to Lawford? Well, he were a bit short tempered, and him and his man soon fell out and he told him to take himself off.

"Where tew?" says Sam.

"Oh, go to Hell," shouts old Charley.

So Sam went off, and when next day came he never turned up to work.

The next day he came back, and old Charley says, "And where've you been?"

"Oh," says Sam, "I went there where you telled me."

"Oh ah," says old Charley, "and where be that then?"

"To Hell," says Sam, helping him along nicely. "'Twasn't at all a bad place, and there were a lovely great fire, and a row of chairs, so I went and I sat down. Then in comes the Devil, with his horns and pitchfork, and says, 'Here you, out of that, quick. We're keeping that armchair for old Charley Creed.'"

·83· The Hungry Mowers

Printed by Edward M. Wilson in "Some Humorous English Folk Tales, Part II," Folk-Lore, XLIX (1938), 279–80, No. 16, as told in September, 1936, by Richard Harrison, who heard the tale from Darwin Leighton of Kendal, who had heard it in Berkshire.

Type 1567G, Good Food Changes Song and Motif J1341.11, "Hired men sing of displeasure with food; change song when food is improved" are reported only for Finland (five texts), England (three) and the United States (six). Baughman comments on the cante-fable form often taken by this type. The master-man becomes a master-slave relationship in Southern Negro tradition; see R. M. Dorson, Negro Folktales in Michigan (Cambridge, Mass., 1956), pp. 67–68, "The Mean Boss," and note 37, p. 213.

"Tommy-shop" is a job where the workers are fed. "Wake" is weak. "Tewit" is plover. "Hod" is hold.

· THERE WAS ONCE a farmer who had a lot of hay, and he had to hire a lot of men to get it cut down. It wasn't a very good Tommy-shop (for the wife was a bit greedy and gave them sloppy stuff for breakfast, curds and whey and such-like), but the men didn't know that. He managed to get about nine men who started off next day. T'farmer thought they were a bit slow over their job, so he thought he would go and see what they did and how fast they were getting on. So as he peeped over the hedge he could hear them singing:

> Curds and whey
> Ivery day.
> Curds and whey
> Ivery day.

So he ran home right away, and told his wife she wasn't feeding them half plenty. "They are as wake as tewits; they can hardly hod their lays."

And t'wife said, "They git a girt dinner ivery neet, an' plenty to eat through t'day, so they shouldn't tak' much 'urt wi' that."

But t'boss said tul 'er, "I's maister here. Tha gits tha girt 'am down an' tha fills t'biggest pan reet full, an' tha mun do about fowerteen eggs for t'brikfast in t'mornin'. And tha'll see a girt change 'll 'appen when they've itten that."

"Ay, why," she said, "I'll likely hev to do as I's tellt."

Next mornin' when they co' down for brikfast, they seed a girt dish full o' ham an' eggs. So they started breakfast, and when they'd finished there was nowt left o' t'dish. So off they started to mow their hay again, and t'boss said to t'missis, "I'll away up and see what happens this time." An' when he peeped ower t'hedge they were goin' like a steam engine:

> 'Am an' eggs
> Mind thi legs.
> 'Am an' eggs
> Mind thi legs.

·84· *The Farmer and His Ox*

Recorded from Ruth L. Tongue, September 28, 1963, as she heard this spoof about 1906 in Somerset.

This seems to be a short form of Type 1705, Talking Horse and Dog, reported only for the United States, in Baughman's index. His earliest reference is to a 1925 text from South Carolina. Motif B210.1, "Person frightened by animals successively replying to his remarks," also fits.

Eric Partridge examined this genre in The "Shaggy Dog" Story: its Origin, Development and Nature (*London, 1953*). *Collected texts were classified and analysed by Jan Harold Brunvand in "A Classification of Shaggy Dog Stories,"* Journal of American Folklore, *LXXVI (1963), 42–68. I follow his classification in these few examples. It seems likely that the true shaggy dog story was brought to England by the American air-*

men. *I heard the first two when I was in the Air Force about 1944, and these both seemed rather American in type: B300.2, "The Poker-Playing Dog," and B210, "The Talking Dog and Horse," in this case slightly altered. About 1948 I heard "The Two Elephants" (No. 85) which seems more English in tone, and in 1953 we were subjected to a deluge of shaggy dog stories, many of them belonging to Section D, "Hoax Stories," long elaborate narrations of which the point is that they are pointless. The tellers have now forgotten most of these stories, but two of them have retold "The Tortoises' Picnic" (No. 88) and "The Horse Who Played Cricket" (No. 86). The fashion for these stories seems to be waning in England, but they are still told by oldish schoolchildren, and possibly by undergraduates.*

· THERE WERE A zurly old varmer and 'e 'ad a girt ox. One day 'e said to it, "Thee girt orkurd vule. Stupid vule thou be, I wonder who taught thee to be so orkurd!"

And the ox 'e turn round to varmer, and 'e say, "Why, it were thee, tha' girt stupid vule!"

·85· *The Two Elephants*

Told to Katharine M. Briggs at Comrie, Perthshire, in 1948 by John Innes, originally from Glasgow, and recently separated from the Navy.

This falls under Brunvand's general category, B400–B499, "Stories About Animals and Humans—Miscellaneous," although the present example is lacking. Motif B211, "Animal uses human speech," is present here as in other shaggy dogs. The current fad for elephant jokes has resulted in The Elephant Book *by Lennie Weintraub, Leonard Stern, and Larry Sloan (Los Angeles, 1963), and* There's an Elephant in My Sandwich *by Marcie Hans and Lynne Babcock (New York, 1963).*

· AN EXPLORER WAS going through the jungle. He had gone a very long way along a narrow track when he saw an elephant.

It was sitting quite still facing him, with its front feet together, very upright and quite quiet. He went by it cautiously, but it never stirred. He went on for miles and miles and miles and then he came to another elephant, with its back to him this time, but in the very same attitude as the first one. He was so surprised that he said aloud, "Whatever are you two doing?"

"Hush," said the elephant, "don't disturb us, we're playing at being bookends."

•86•   *The Horse Who Played Cricket*

Heard by Katharine M. Briggs in York from a Londoner of Welsh extraction, Piers Nash-Williams, on August 8, 1963.

This is Brunvand's B350.1, "Horse Plays Cricket, It Can't Bowl," placed in the category "Clever Animals With One Flaw." Brunvand cites Eric Partridge, The "Shaggy Dog" Story, *pp. 70–74; John Waller,* Shaggy Dog and other Surrealist Fables *(London, 1953), pp. 40–41; and the CBS Radio files in New York City accumulated from a shaggy dog contest held in March and April, 1958.*

• THERE WAS ONCE a visiting cricket team—a town team—that went out to play against a country team. And just at the last moment as they got on to the 'bus, they got a message from one of the team that he had broken his leg and couldn't come. They hadn't a spare man, and they hadn't time to look for one, so the only thing was to hope that there might be some spare players in the home team, and they could borrow one. When they got to the place, the captain of the visiting team explained how it was, and asked the captain of the home team if he could borrow any member of the club for the game. "I'm awfully sorry," said the home captain, "we're such a small club that all our members are playing. I don't know what we can do. Oh! I know, go and ask that old horse over there if he'll stand in for you. He's drawn the mower and the roller for years, and there isn't anything he doesn't know about cricket. He's a good-natured old chap; go over and ask him nicely, and I'm sure he'll consent."

So the captain of the visiting team walked over to the horse, and he said, "Excuse me, sir, the captain thinks you might be willing to oblige us. One of the team's failed at the last moment, and the captain thought you might be willing to play for us. We don't like to go home without a game at all."

"Well, I'm terribly out of practice," said the horse, "but I don't like to be disobliging. I'll tell you what; put me down to bat last, and then I can't do much harm."

So that was arranged. The home team won the toss, and they put the visiting team in to bat first. They may have been a small club, but every man of them was a cricketer, as the visiting team soon discovered. They had a couple of demon bowlers who knocked the wickets down like ninepins, and soon there were nine wickets down, with about twice as many runs. It was the old horse's turn to go in, and soon the visiting team's spirits began to rise, for he knocked those bowlers all over the field. The score went to twenty, thirty, forty, fifty, and it looked as if the old horse would stay there till he'd made his century, only unfortunately the tenth man got caught out, and that was the end of the innings. After this, the home team went in, and they soon showed they were as good at batting as they were at bowling, and the visiting captain put on every bowler they had, and they were all treated with contempt. At last, he went over to the old horse, who was fielding long-stop.

"You've done so well for us in the batting, sir," he said, "I wonder if you would try what you can do with the bowling?"

The old horse looked at him, and he threw back his head, and laughed and laughed. "Bowling!" he said, "who ever heard of a horse bowling at cricket?"

·87· *The Pious Lion*

Heard by Katharine M. Briggs in 1963 at Burford from Margaret Nash-Williams.

12

This also falls under Brunvand's B400–B439, "Stories About Animals and Humans—Miscellaneous," without a specific place. A reverse twist is here given to a comic tale in which a frightened man imitates the actions of a bear he encounters; when the bear defecates, the man says he is ahead of him (R. M. Dorson, "Dialect Stories of the Upper Peninsula," Journal of American Folklore, LXI [1948], 127–28, No. 21, "The Bear on Sugar Island").

· THERE WAS A man walking in the jungle. I don't know if he was a missionary or an explorer, but, at any rate, he had no gun with him. Suddenly he met a lion face to face. He knew that if he turned to run, the lion would be on him in a minute, and he had heard that if you stared hard at an animal it would grow uneasy and slink away. So he fixed the lion with his eye. He stared at the lion and the lion stared at him, and so they stood for about five minutes. Then the lion put its paws close together on the ground, and bent its head right down over them. This seemed a bit more hopeful, but the man was pretty nearly hypnotized by this time, and he thought the best thing he could do was to imitate the lion. So he bent his head down over his hands. So they stood for another five minutes.

Then the lion lifted its head and said, "I don't know what you're doing, but I'm saying grace."

·88· *The Tortoises' Picnic*

Told to Katharine M. Briggs in August, 1963, in Kent by Celia Downes, about 26, who had previously told her the story when she was 14.

Under B500, The Turtle that was sent Back, Brunvand cites eleven texts. There is an Australian version in Partridge, The "Shaggy Dog" Story, pp. 82–83; and an English locale in Bennett Cerf, Laughing Stock (New York, 1945), p. 59.

· THERE WERE ONCE three tortoises—a father, a mother, and a

baby. And one fine spring day they decided that they would like to go for a picnic. They picked the place they would go to, a nice wood at some distance off, and they began to get their stuff together. They got tins of salmon and tins of tongue, and sandwiches, and orange squash, and everything they could think of. In about three months they were ready, and they set out, carrying their baskets.

They walked and walked and walked, and time went on, and after about eighteen months they sat down and had a rest. But they knew just where they wanted to go and they were about halfway to it, so they set out again. And in three years they reached the picnic place. They unpacked their baskets and spread out the cloth, and arranged the food on it and it looked lovely.

Then Mother Tortoise began to look into the picnic baskets. She turned them all upside down, and shook them, but they were all empty, and at last she said, "We've forgotten the tin-opener!" They looked at each other, and at last Father and Mother said, "Baby, you'll have to go back for it." "What!" said the baby, "me! Go back all that long way!" "Nothing for it," said Father Tortoise, "we can't start without a tin-opener. We'll wait for you." "Well, do you swear, do you promise faithfully," said the baby, "that you won't touch a thing till I come back?" "Yes, we promise faithfully," they said, and Baby plodded away, and after a while he was lost to sight among the bushes.

And Father and Mother waited. They waited and waited and waited, and a whole year went by, and they began to get rather hungry. But they'd promised, so they waited. And another year went by, and another, and they got really hungry. "Don't you think we could have just one sandwich each?" said Mother Tortoise. "He'd never know the difference." "No," said Father Tortoise, "we promised. We must wait till he comes back."

So they waited, and another year passed, and another, and they got ravenous.

"It's six years now," said Mother Tortoise. "He ought to be back by now."

"Yes, I suppose he ought," said Father Tortoise. "Let's just have one sandwich while we're waiting."

They picked up the sandwiches, but just as they were going

to eat them, a little voice said, "Aha! I knew you'd cheat." And
Baby Tortoise popped his head out of a bush. "It's a good thing
I didn't start for that tin-opener," he said.

•*89*• *The Dog and the Hares*

*Printed by Edward M. Wilson in "Some Humorous English
Folk Tales, Part I," Folk-Lore, XLIX (1938), 191–92, No. 12,
as told by James D. Harrison in Crosthwaite, September, 1936.
He had heard it at the bar of the Royal Hotel, Bowness, Winder-
mere, Westmorland.*

*Type 1889L, Lie: the Split Dog (Motif X1215.11) is a
Münchausen tall tale, unreported however from European countries. Baughman cites only the present text from England, but
has examples from a dozen American states. The earliest is from
an 1808 jestbook.*

*Regional variants are given in R. M. Dorson, American Folk-
lore (Chicago, 1959), pp. 41, 81, 108, 229, and an Illinois text is
printed in Dorson, Buying the Wind, pp. 347–48, "Davy
Crockett and Old Bounce." Evidence that this and other tall tales
circulate in Europe is given by Gustav Hennigsen in "Kunsten
at Lyve Lodret," Nordisk Institut for Folkedigtning, Studier
No. 1 (København, 1961), 1–39.*

*"Lay" is a scythe-blade. "Smoot" is a hole in the bottom of a
wall for hares and rabbits to go through.*

• A MAN WAS bragging about his dog. His companion said he had
a better dog than that, his was a whippet, and a grand dog for
rabbitin', a terrible dog for hares—and he would take this man
with him to shew him what this dog would do. So they went
up intull a field where they knew there was some hares, and they
would try it. But he said, "We'll take a lay along wi' us."

"What'll we want wi' a lay?"

"Oh!" he said, "we might need it."

So he knocked the lay out o' t'pole, and he would just want
t'blade and didn't want t'pole. So away they went up into this

field. Ye know there's a smoot hole through t'wa' at t'bottom of t'field, and hares generally went through that smoot—he knew that. So he put t'lay in wi' t'point facing t'same way that t'hare was coming, and so they went up t'breast and loosed t'dog. T'dog put a hare up directly and away they went down t'field towards t'smoot; another hare jump up and followed. But instead of t'hares goin' through t'smoot, they jump the wall. But the dog took to t'smoot, and went through and split itself in two—it was going that fast—and one half went after one hare and one half went after the other.

·90· *The Man Who Bounced*

Recorded from Ruth L. Tongue, September 28, 1963, as she heard the tale in Somerset.

The general category is Type 1920, Contest in Lying. Cf. "Boasting of One's Own Region," in R. M. Dorson, Folk Legends of Japan (Tokyo and Rutland, Vt. 1962), p. 207.

Baughman under Motif X1021.1(a), "Man falls with rubber boots on, bounces without stopping. He is shot to keep him from starving to death," gives seven American references from the Midwest and the Far West. The super-cowboy Pecos Bill had to shoot his first wife Slue-Foot Sue when his horse threw her and she bounced for ten days on her steel bustle: Motif X1021 (aa).

The present variant is the first reported from England.

· THERE WERE A stranger come to the village, and everything 'e saw, 'e knew something better. Trees in 'is country was 'igher, bridges was bigger, rivers was wider, and cliffs, well! They was real 'igh. And 'e were a-talking about someone as fell off a cliff, up 'is way, and 'ow 'e'd caught fire as 'e was falling down, it were such a long way down.

Well, one o' they as was listening says, "Oh! ay. Now we got a cliff down country, and there were a little vat yellow, round as a apple 'e were, and 'e were walking on top o' cliff, wind took and caught 'en, and blowed 'en over. Well! when 'e got to bottom, 'e bounced. 'E bounced up a 'undred feet, 'e come down and 'e bounced up fifty feet. And what's more the poor little vellow, 'e went on a-bouncing and a-bouncing, for a week, and they 'ad to shoot 'un."

•91• *Mark Twain in the Fens*

Recorded from W. H. Barrett, October 12, 1963, as he heard the anecdote in the Cambridgeshire Fens.

This tradition of Mark Twain's tall talk belongs to Type 1920A, a subtype of 1920, Contest in Lying, and includes Type 1960D, The Great Vegetable. Related motifs are X1435.1, "Lie: large potatoes," and X1301, "Lie: the great fish." Both types are familiar in Europe and the United States. Baughman cites variants of the great vegetable and the great kettle from ten states. A Cornish text brought to Michigan is printed by R. M. Dorson in the Journal of American Folklore, *LXI (1948), 138–39.*

An example of Type 1920, "The Tall Tale of the Merchant's Son," is in D. Noy, Folktales of Israel, *a companion volume in this series, No. 24, pp. 56–58.*

Mark Twain made a very favorable impression in the Fens because he had known hardship in his youth.

• WHEN I WAS a boy some Dons of Cambridge brought Mark Twain to a little pub near my home, to recover from a nervous breakdown. Well, he and the old Fenmen got on well together. Mark could tell a very fine yarn. He told those old fishermen that Americans never went fishing unless they took a mill with them. When the Fenmen asked what the mill was for, Mark replied that the fish were so large that no man could pull 'em out, so they had to use a mill.

A short time afterwards, Mark saw a team of horses standing outside a blacksmith's forge, and he said to old Chafer Legge the Fenman, "What are those horses waiting for?" Chafer said, "They're waiting for the man that's just going out fishing."

Another time, when the landlord of the Ship Inn where he

was staying showed him some large potatoes, Mark said, "Call
them spuds? You ought to see what we grow in America!
They're so large that we can only get one into a saucepan at a
time!" That evening a barge came along up the river, with a
great big water-tube boiler for Cambridge gasworks. They
moored it into the bank, aside of the Ship Inn. Mark went out
and he saw this huge boiler lashed on the deck of the barge, and
he said to the landlord, "What is that?"

"Oh!" the landlord said, "That's nothing. 'Tis just one of our
saucepans we boil potatoes in." Oh! he was a humorous old man!

·92· *The Endless Tale*

*Heard by Katharine M. Briggs from Grace Crowder in 1919 in
Perthshire.*

*This comes under Type 2320, Rounds (Motif Z17), of which
112 instances are reported for Lithuania. Baughman gives
examples collected in half a dozen states.*

*There are several variants of this tale. One heard in 1922 at
a Girl Guide campfire began, "It was a dark and stormy night
and the robbers came in two by two," etc.*

*A song that was popular at that time to the tune of "For He's
a Jolly Good Fellow" went as follows:*

> The bear went over the mountain   (*repeat twice*)
> To see what he could see.
>
> And what do you think he saw?   (*repeat*)
> The other side of the mountain   (*repeat twice*)
> Was all that he could see.
>
> So what do you think he did?   (*repeat*)
> He went back over the mountain.   *etc.*

· IT WAS A dark and stormy night, and the Captain stood on the
bridge, and he said to the Mate, "Tell us a yarn."

And the Mate began, "It was a dark and stormy night, and
the Captain stood on the bridge, and he said to the Mate, 'Tell
us a yarn.' And the Mate began," etc.

Glossary

Allerntide All Hallows or Hallowe'en.

barton A byre or cow-shed.

batch A piece of open common land or moorland.

beck A stream.

croom'le Crumble.

dairy maid A white and tortoise-shell cat.

Dandy dogs *See* wild hunt.

dew-bit An early morning snack.

diddicky Rotten.

drashel A threshold.

drinking Elevenses.

dunk A donkey.

fither Whether.

four-wents A crossroads.

Gabriel ratchets *See* wild hunt.

galley-trap The Somerset name for a fairy ring. The local belief is that if a thief or a murderer sets a foot in it, he will come to the gallows.

gladdon An iris, one of the sedge family.

hafe Half.

hobbled West Quantock dialect for lameness in a woman.

hod Hold.

hose-bud A rascal.

hurd-yed A red-head. In Somerset, red-headed men are always regarded with mistrust.

intack An enclosure.

lay A scythe-blade.

leeat Late.

lile Little.

maw'r or *mawther*   A Suffolk dialect word for daughter or
    young maid.

may   A young girl, a maid.

mools   Soil.

'natomy   A skeleton.

nummet   A midday snack.

nursey   To have a child.

parson   A signpost, for a road.

pop-weasel   To grow angry and scold.

quarter-ail   Paralysis.

rhines   The deep ditches on the sides of the roads.

roadster   A tramp.

robin herdick   A robin redbreast.

scramble-footed   West Quantock dialect for lameness in a horse.

seeaf   Safe.

shut   To shoot.

smoot   A hole in the bottom of the field wall for hares and
    rabbits to go through.

spud   Turf.

Spunkies   Will-'o-the-wisps or marsh lights; *Ignis fatuus*. These
    are often believed to be fairies, ghosts, or malevolent spirits
    who lead people astray, but they also appear as friendly
    spirits on occasion.

steart-horse   A mud sledge.

steean   A stone.

sucker   A young foal.

tallat   An attic or loft.

ta-morn   Tomorrow.

teddies   Potatoes.

tewit   A plover.

thruff   Through.

tommy-shop   A job where the workers are fed.

till   To, towards, or until.

unket   Uncanny.

urchin   A hedgehog.

wake   Weak.

wild hunt A ghostly hunter and his rout continue the chase. This belief is well-known throughout Europe, especially in the north. Superstitions connected with it—such as the means of avoiding its power, the identity of its leader, and the time of its appearance—vary from place to place. Its character, however, is always malevolent. *See* Gabriel ratchets, Yeth hounds, and Dandy dogs.

yam Home.

yarth Earth.

Yeth hounds *See* wild hunt.

zogs Bogland.

Bibliography

AARNE, ANTTI. *Schwänke über schwerhörige Menschen.* (Folklore Fellows Communications, No. 20.) Mamina, 1914.

ADAM DE LA HALLE. *Jeu Adam ou de la Feuillée. Oeuvres Complètes du Trouvère Adam de la Halle.* Paris, 1872.

ADDY, SIDNEY O. "Four Yorkshire Tales," *Folk-Lore*, VIII (1897), 393–396.

———. *Household Tales and Other Traditional Remains.* London and Sheffield, 1895.

ANDERSON, WALTER. *Kaiser und Abt.* (Folklore Fellows Communications, No. 42.) Helsinki, 1923.

AUBREY, JOHN. *Hypomnemata Antiquaria* A. MS Bodley, Aubrey 3.

———. *Miscellanies upon Various Subjects.* 5th ed. London, 1890.

———. *Remaines of Gentilisme and Judaisme.* London, 1687.

BALFOUR, M. C. "Legends of the Lincolnshire Cars," *Folk-Lore*, II (1891), 145–170, 257–283, 401–418.

BARING-GOULD, SABINE. *The Lives of the Saints.* Rev. ed. 16 vols. London, 1914.

BARRETT, W. H. *Tales from the Fens*, ed. Enid Porter. London, 1963.

———. *More Tales from the Fens*, ed. Enid Porter. London, 1964.

BAUGHMAN, ERNEST W. *A Type and Motif-Index of the Folktales of England and North America.* (Indiana University Folklore Series, No. 21) The Hague: Mouton and Co., 1965.

BAXTER, RICHARD. *The Certainty of the World of Spirits.* London, 1691.

BEAUMONT, CYRIL W. *Puppets and Puppetry.* London, 1958.

BELLOC, HILAIRE. *The Four Men: A Farrago.* London, 1902.

BELLOC, HILAIRE. *James the Second*. London, 1928.

BLACK, C. E. *County Folk-Lore, No. 3, Orkney and Shetland*, ed. N. W. Thomas. London, 1903.

BOGGS, RALPH STEELE. "North Carolina White Folktales and Riddles," *Journal of American Folklore*, XLVII (1934), 289–328.

BOLTE, JOHANNES, and POLÍVKA, GEORG. *Anmerkungen zu den Kinder und Hausmärchen der Brüder Grimm*. 5 vols. Leipzig, 1913–31.

BOVET, R. *Pandaemonium or the Devil's Cloyster*. London, 1684.

BRAY, MRS. A. E. *The Borders of the Tamar and the Tavy*. 2 vols. London, 1879.

BRIGGS, KATHARINE M. *The Anatomy of Puck*. London, 1959.

———. *Pale Hecate's Team*. London, 1962.

BROWN, W. N. "The Silence Wager Stories, their Origin and Diffusion," *American Journal of Philology*, LXIII (1922), 289–317.

BRUNVAND, JAN H. "A Classification for Shaggy Dog Stories," *Journal of American Folklore*, LXXVI (1963), 42–68.

BURNE, CHARLOTTE S., and JACKSON, GEORGINA. *Shropshire Folk-Lore*. London, 1883.

BUTLER, E. M. *The Myth of the Magus*. New York, 1948.

———. *Ritual Magic*. Cambridge, 1949.

CAMPBELL, MARIE. *Tales from the Cloud Walking Country*. Bloomington, 1958.

CERF, BENNETT. *Laughing Stock*. New York, 1945.

CHAMBERS, ROBERT. *The Popular Rhymes of Scotland*. Edinburgh, 1890.

CHILD, FRANCIS J. *The English and Scottish Popular Ballads*. 3 vols. New York, 1957.

CHRISTIANSEN, REIDAR TH. (ed.). *Folktales of Norway*. Chicago and London, 1964.

———. *The Migratory Legends*. (Folklore Fellows Communications, No. 175.) Helsinki, 1958.

CLODD, EDWARD. "The Philosophy of Rumpelstiltskin," *"Folk-Lore Journal*, VII (1889), 135–163.

———. *Tom Tit Tot*. London, 1898.

CLOUSTON, W. A. *The Book of Noodles*. London, 1888.

CRAIGIE, W. A. *Scandinavian Folk-Lore*. London, 1896.

COX, MARIAN R. *Cinderella*. London, 1893.

DE LA MARE, WALTER. *Come Hither*. New York, 1923.

DISHER, MAURICE W. *Victorian Song: from Dive to Drawing Room*. London, 1955.

DORSON, RICHARD M. *American Folklore*. Chicago, 1959.

———. *Bloodstoppers and Bearwalkers*. Cambridge, Mass., 1952.

———. *Buying the Wind*. Chicago, 1964.

———. "Dialect Stories of the Upper Peninsula," *Journal of American Folklore*, LXI (1948), 113–150.

———. *Folk Legends of Japan*. Tokyo and Rutland, Vt., 1962.

———. *Jonathan Draws the Long Bow*. Cambridge, Mass., 1946.

———. *Negro Folktales in Michigan*. Cambridge, Mass., 1956.

———. *Negro Tales from Pine Bluff, Arkansas and Calvin, Michigan*. (Indiana University Folklore Series, No. 12.) Bloomington, Indiana., 1958.

———. "Polish Tales from Joe Woods," *Western Folklore*, VIII (1949), 131–145.

EVANS, E. ESTYN. *Irish Folk-Ways*. London, 1957.

FIELD, JOHN E. *The Myth of the Pent Cuckoo*. London, 1913.

The Frank C. Brown Collection of North Carolina Folklore, ed. Newman Ivey White. 7 vols. Durham, North Carolina, 1952–64.

GIRALDUS CAMBRENSIS. *Itinerary Through Wales*. London, 1863.

GOMME, ALICE B. "The Green Lady," *Folk-Lore*, VII (1896), 411–414.

———. *The Traditional Games of England, Scotland and Ireland*. London, 1894–98.

GRIMM, JAKOB L. K. and WILHELM. *Grimm's Household Tales*, tr. and ed. Margaret Hunt. 2 vols. London, 1884; new ed., New York, 1944.

GRIMM, J. *Teutonic Mythology*, tr. J. S. Stallybrass. 3 vols. London, 1882–83.

GUTCH, ELIZA. *County Folk-Lore, No. 2, The North Riding of Yorkshire*. London, 1901.

HALLIWELL-PHILLIPPS, JAMES O. *Nursery Rhymes and Popular Tales*. London, 1849.

———. *The Nursery Rhymes of England*. London, 1843.

HARTLAND, EDWIN SIDNEY. *English Fairy and other Folk Tales.* London, 1890.

———. *County Folk-Lore, No. 1, Folk-Lore of Gloucestershire.* London, 1892.

———. "Peeping Tom and Lady Godiva," *Folk-Lore,* I (1890), 207–226.

HENDERSON, WILLIAM. *Notes on the Folk-Lore of the Northern Counties of England and the Borders.* London, 1879.

HENNINGSEN, GUSTAV. "Kunsten and Lyve Lodret," *Nordisk Institut for Folkedigtning,* Studier I. København, 1961.

HOFFMAN-KRAYER, E., and BÄCHTOLD-STÄUBLI, H. (eds.). *Handwörterbuch des deutschen Aberglaubens.* 10 vols. Berlin and Leipzig, 1927–42.

HOLE, CHRISTINA. *English Folk-Lore.* London, 1940.

HUNT, ROBERT. *Popular Romances of the West of England.* 2 vols. London, 1865.

HUTCHINSON, WILLIAM. *The History of the County of Cumberland.* 2 vols. Carlisle, 1794.

IRVING, H. B. "Jack White's Gibbet," *Somerset Year Book.* London, 1922.

JACOBS, JOSEPH. *English Fairy Tales.* London, 1890.

———. *More English Fairy Tales.* London, 1894.

JAMIESON, ROBERT. *Illustrations of Northern Antiquities,* 1814.

KEIGHTLEY, THOMAS. *The Fairy Mythology.* London, 1860.

KENNEDY, PATRICK. *Legendary Fictions of the Irish Celts.* London, 1886.

The Khoja: Tales of Nasr-ed-Din, tr. Henry D. Barnham. New York, 1924.

KIRKLAND, EDWIN C. "The American Redaction of Tale Type 922," *Fabula,* IV (1961), 248–259.

KITTREDGE, GEORGE LYMAN. *Witchcraft in Old and New England.* Cambridge, Mass., 1929.

KOSKO, MARIA. "L'Auberge de Jérusalem," *Fabula,* IV (1961), 81–97.

———. "Varia à propos du Malentendu," *Comparative Literature,* X (1958), 267–377.

KRISTENSEN, EVALD TANG. *Danske Sagn.* 6 vols. København, 1928–39.

LANG, ANDREW. "Cap o' Rushes," *Folk-Lore,* I (1890), 295–299.

LIUNGMAN, WALDEMAR. *Sveriges Samtliga Folksagor.* 3 vols. Djursholm, 1950–52.

MacDOUGALL, JAMES, and CALDER, GEORGE. *Folk Tales and Fairy Lore in Gaelic and English.* Edinburgh, 1910.

MONTGOMERIE, N. and W. *The Well at the World's End.* London, 1956.

MOTHERWELL, WILLIAM. *Minstrelsy Ancient and Modern.* Edinburgh, 1827.

NOY, DOV. (ed.). *Folktales of Israel.* Chicago and London, 1963.

PARTRIDGE, ERIC. *The 'Shaggy Dog' Story, Its Origin, Development and Nature.* London, 1953.

PEELE, GEORGE. *The Old Wives' Tale.* London, 1595.

POTTER, BEATRIX. *The Tale of Squirrel Nutkin.* London, 1903.

RADFORD, E. and M. A. *Encyclopedia of Superstitions.* New York, 1949.

RANDOLPH, VANCE. *Who Blowed Up the Church House?* New York, 1952.

ROOTH, A. B. *The Cinderella Cycle.* Lund, 1951.

ROSENBERG, NEIL. "An Annotated Collection of Parrot Jokes" (Master's thesis, Indiana University, June, 1964).

SAINTYVES, PIERRE. *Les Saints, Successeurs des Dieux.* Paris, 1907.

SCOT, REGINALD. *Discoverie of Witchcraft,* 1584 and 3rd Edition 1665.

SEKI, KEIGO (ed.). *Folktales of Japan.* Chicago and London, 1963.

SIKES, WIRT. *British Goblins.* London, 1880.

STEPHENS, JAMES. *In the Land of Youth.* London, 1924.

THISELTON-DYER, T. F. *English Folk-Lore.* London, 1878.

THOMPSON, STITH. *The Folktale.* New York, 1946.

———. *Motif-Index of Folk Literature.* 6 vols. Rev. ed. Copenhagen and Bloomington, Ind., 1955–58.

THOMPSON, STITH, and AARNE, ANTTI. *The Types of the Folktale: A Classification and Bibliography.* (Folklore Fellows Communications, No. 180.) Helsinki, 1961.

TONGUE, R. L. "The Open Grave," *Folklore,* LXXIII (1962), 106–108.

TONGUE, R. L. "Somerset Folklore." Folklore Society (1965).

TUTCHIN, JOHN. *The Bloody Assizes*, ed. J. J. Muddiman. Edinburgh, 1929.

WALLER, JOHN. *Shaggy Dog and other Surrealist Fables*. London, 1953.

WILLIAM OF MALMESBURY. *Chronicle of the Kings of England*. London, 1847.

WILSON, EDWARD M. "Some Humorous English Folk Tales, Part I," *Folk-Lore*, XLIX (1938), 182–192; "Part II," 277–286; "Part III," *Folk-Lore*, LIV (1943), 258–261.

WOOLLCOTT, ALEXANDER. *While Rome Burns*. New York, 1934.

ZÖNG-IN-SÖB. *Folk-Tales from Korea*. London, 1952.

Index of Motifs

(Motif numbers are from Stith Thompson, *Motif-Index of Folk Literature* [6 vols.; Bloomington, Ind., 1955–58]. [B] after a title indicates a new number assigned by Ernest W. Baughman, *A Type and Motif-Index of the Folktales of England and North America* [Indiana University Folklore Series, No. 21; The Hague: Mouton and Co., 1965].)

A. MYTHOLOGICAL MOTIFS

Motif No.		*Tale No.*
A661.0.1.2	Saint Peter as porter of Heaven	56
A977.1	Giant responsible for certain stones	30
A977.2	Devil throws stones	31

B. ANIMALS

B210.1	Person frightened by animals successively replying to his remarks	84
B211	Animal uses human speech	85
B251.1.2	Animals speak to one another at Christmas	13
B470.1	Small fish as helper	2
B651.1	Marriage to fox in human form	43
B733.2	Dogs howling ominous of death	22

C. TABU

C411.1	Tabu: asking for reason of an unusual action	24
C420.2	Tabu: not to speak about a certain happening	16
C495.2.2	"We Three," "For gold," "That is right"	70

D. MAGIC

D950.10	Magic apple tree	14
D1123	Magic ship	44
D1272	Magic circle	9
D1273.1.3	Seven as a magic number	17
D1273.1.5	Twelve as a magic number	19
D1278.1	Magic churchyard mould	24, 55
D1318.5.2	Corpse bleeds when murderer touches it	46
D1470.1	Magic wishing object causes wishes to be fulfilled	7
D1810.8.3.2	Dream warns of danger which will happen in near future	28

Z. MISCELLANEOUS GROUPS OF MOTIFS

SHAGGY DOG STORIES

From Jan Harold Brunvand, "A Classification for Shaggy Dog Stories," *Journal of American Folklore*, LXXVI (1963), 42–68.

Index of Tale Types

Type numbers are from Antti Aarne and Stith Thompson, *The Types of the Folktale: A Classification and Bibliography* [Folklore Fellows Communications, No. 180, Helsinki, 1961]. [B] after a title indicates a new number assigned by Ernest W. Baughman, *A Type and Motif-Index of the Folktales of England and North America* (Indiana University Folklore Series, No. 21; The Hague: Mouton and Co., 1965).

General Index

Aarne, Antti (Finnish folklorist), xvii, 128
Aberdeen, Scotland, 26
Addy, Sidney O. (English folklorist), xv, xvi, xxix, 3, 26, 49, 55, 116, 117
Aesop, vii
Anderson, Walter (Estonian folklorist), 119
Animals, magic, supernatural, or unusual: bird, as soul of dead girl, 28; cat, as transformed witch, 57; cattle, change to pixies, 56; dog, changes to man, 3–5, split, 146–47; donkey, talking, 45–46, protected from evil, 51; elephant, talking, 141; fish, helpful, 8–9, talking, 3; goose, lays golden eggs, 3; horse, leg of removed for reshoeing, 79, of ghost, 108–109, plays cricket, 142–43, spirit, 78; hounds, of Devil, 53–54; lion, talking, 144; ox, charmed, 45, talking, 45–46, 141; rabbit, changes to woman, 53–54
Apple-Tree Man: frightens cat, 47; given cider, 45, 47; reveals treasure, 45–46; mentioned, xxiv
Arabian tradition, 130
Archives: of the School of Scottish Studies, xxvi, 118. *See also* Indiana University Folklore Archives
Asbjörnsen, Peter Christen (Norwegian folklorist), vii, viii
Ash, John (informant), 55, 71
Asian tradition, 125, 130, 134. *See also* Ceylonese, Chinese, Korean *and* Japanese tradition
Aubrey, John (English folklorist), ix, xxvi, xxviii, 62, 77
Australia, 64–65
Australian tradition, vii, 144

Badcock, Walter (informant), 71, 72
Balfour, Marie Clothilde (English folklorist), xviii, xxiii, xxix, 39
Ballads: stories adapted into folktales, vii; widespread in England, v; "Clerk Colvil", 54; "The Derby Ram", xvi; "Get Up and Bar the Door", 130; "King John and the Bishop", 119; "The Queen of Elfan's Nourice", 38; "Tam Lin", 38
Baring-Gould, Sabine (English folklorist), xvii, 26, 78
Barrett, W. H. (informant), xxi, xxx, 59, 81, 84, 110, 148

Baughman, Ernest W. (American folklore indexer), 3, 6, 17, 27, 39, 62, 64, 66, 89, 90, 94, 95, 97, 98, 101, 109, 113, 115, 116, 117, 123, 125, 127, 128, 129, 132, 133, 134, 137, 138, 139, 140, 146, 147, 148, 149
Baxter, Richard (English Puritan theologian), 62
Bayliss, Fred (informant), 66
Belgian tradition, 113
Belloc, Hilaire, 76, 95
Berkshire, 138
Black, G. F. (English folklorist), 38
Blacksmith: St. Aloys, removes horse's leg, 78–79; St. Dunstan, pinches Devil's nose, 76–77; mentioned, 79, 148
Bland, Mrs. J. E. (informant), 133
Blindness: believed to be caused by banana, 123; caused by fairies, 39
Blood: pixy, 80; ritually smeared on doorsill, 40
Bødker, Laurits (Danish folklorist), 99
Bogey: dances with witch, 9; grants wish, 44; guardian of fields, 41; outwitted, 29; propitiated by farmers, 39–44 *passim*; powerless before cross, 51; mentioned, ix, xiv, xvi
Boswell, Taimie (informant), 16
Brand, John (English antiquary), v, vi, xii
Bray, Mrs. A. E. (English literary folklorist), vii–xiv *passim*, 38, 52, 55, 94
Bread: saint's, restored when eaten, 75; used in harvest rite, 40–43 *passim*
Bride: dies on wedding day, 88; fits glass slipper, 25; pours half-cup of tea, 100
Briggs, J. (English collector), 128
Briggs, Katharine (English folklorist), xvi–xxi, 33, 55, 67, 98, 100, 101, 113, 121, 123, 141, 142, 143, 144, 149
Briggs, Winifred E. (informant), 99
Brown, Ambrose (informant), 77
Brown, Miss (informant), 71
Brownie, x, xxvi
Brunvand, Jan Harold (American folklorist), 140, 141, 142, 144
Buckinghamshire, 90
Burial: of apparent dead, 89; of bones of murdered stepdaughter, 28; of bones of ghost, 66
Buried treasure: gold, 45–46; jewelry, 84; revealed by Apple-Tree Man, 44–46

Supernatural ability: to foresee future, 18; to put people in trance, 21, 22, 23, 24; to remove trance, 22, 23, 24; to see fairies, 38–39; to see ghosts and spirits, xxix; to wish oneself somewhere or something else, 18–19, 22, 24, 25
  –great skill: imp spins five skeins in one night, 13–16
  –great strength: at jumping, 86–87; in running, 87
Supernatural beings. See Apple-Tree Man, Bogey, Fairy, Green Lady, Pixy, Witch
Suffolk, 10, 129
Sussex, 76, 95, 99
Swedish tradition, 6, 68, 122, 132, 133

Taboo: protects primitive man, x; violated, 4–5, 9, 50
  –nature of: eating fairies' food, 8; looking through keyhole, 7; speaking about a certain happening, 49; speaking to fairy, 88; touching fairy, 88; using fairy ointment, 38; using unkind name, 4, 5; women at fishing grounds, 57
Tasks: answer three questions, 120; assigned by witch, 7–10; guess unusual name, 13–16; run around garden before entering Heaven, 115; spin five skeins in one night, 12–15; write out sins before entering Heaven, 114
Test, bride: fitting glass slipper, 25; pouring half-cup of tea, 100–101
Thiselton-Dyer, T. F. (English folklorist), 50, 58
Thomas, Northcote W. (English folklorist), 38
Thompson, Stith (American folklorist), xvii, xix, 27
Thompson, T. W. (English gipsy-lorist), xxv, 16, 125
  –Notebooks of, xxvi, xxix–xxx, 90, 127
Thoms, William John (English folklorist), v, ix, xii
Tom Tit Tot, xxiii, 13–16
Tongue, Ruth (English folklorist), xx, xxiii, xxvii, xxix, 26, 28, 33, 34, 35, 37, 38, 44, 46, 47, 50, 51, 54, 55, 56, 61, 62, 68, 70, 71, 72, 73, 75, 78, 80, 86, 87, 88, 90, 92, 94, 95, 96, 105, 106, 107, 109, 124, 129, 137, 138, 140, 147
Tortoise: sent on errand, 144–46
Transformations: human into animal: witch into cat, 57; woman into rabbit and back, 63
  –animal into human: dog into young man, 4; rabbit into woman, 54
  –supernatural creature into human: Devil into woman, 77
  –supernatural creature into animal: pixies into cattle, 56; spirit into

horse, 78; spirit into pig, 65. See also Soul
  –object into object: cider mug into silver mug, 34; gold mug into toadstool, 37; leaves into gold, 34; wood chips into ships, 95
Treachery: lover digs grave, 93; sexton digs unneeded grave, 61–62; stepmother makes pies of stepdaughter, 28. See also Death, Deception
Tregeagle, xiv
Trickery: outwitting bogey, 29; misleading greedy brother, 46
Turkish tradition, 130
Tylor, E. B. (English anthropologist), v, x, xv

Ulysses, 54
United States, tradition in: vii, xxii, 27, 39, 44, 55, 88, 89, 90, 116, 117, 133, 139, 140, 146, 148, 149; midwestern, 147; Negro, xxi, 11, 27, 45, 109, 115, 127, 139; New England, 59; Pennsylvania Dutch, 110, 120; Scotch-Irish, 90; southern Appalachians, vi, 17; southwestern, 99–100; western, 147
  –by states: Arkansas, 109, 123; Hawaii, 134; Illinois, 89, 146; Indiana, 90, 127, 137; Kentucky, 3, 6, 79, 90, 137; Maine, 114, 133, 134, 138; Massachusetts, 3, 66, 138; Michigan, 64, 67, 100, 109, 124, 127, 136, 148; Minnesota, 67; Mississippi, 45; Missouri, 64, 90, 134; New Jersey, 39, 127; New Mexico, 134, 137; New York, 3, 17, 39, 129; North Carolina, 3, 11, 45, 90, 128; South Carolina, 128, 140; Tennessee, 90; Texas, 125; Virginia, 3; Wisconsin, 123, 137

Von Sydow, Carl (Swedish folklorist), xx

Wager: 135–36; silence, 130–32
Wales, xx
Walloon tradition, 129
Water: running water protection against evil, 53; used in rain charm, 40
Welsh tradition, 35, 38, 39, 55
West Indian tradition, 117
Westmorland, xx, 115, 116, 119, 122, 128, 130, 132, 133, 134, 135, 146
Widow: frightened of "Summat Queer", 109–10; gives daughter magic clothes, 17–19; helped by St. Wulfric, 73–75
Wild Hunt, 52–54
Wilkinson, T. T. (English folklorist), xvi
William of Newbridge, ix
Wilson, Edward M. (English folklorist), xx, 113, 114, 115, 116, 119, 120, 122, 125, 126, 127, 128, 130, 132, 133, 134, 135, 136, 139, 146